MW00623607

THE SUCCESSFUL CLINICAL MANAGER - HOME HEALTH

JULIA H. MARONEY RN MHSA

Deep Creek Publishers

Published 2022 – Deep Creek Publishers

Copyright © 2022 by Julia H. Maroney

All rights reserved. No part of this publication may be reproduced, stored or transmitted in any form or by any means, electronic, mechanical, photocopying, recording, scanning, or otherwise, without written permission from the publisher. It is illegal to copy this book, post it to a website, or distribute it by other means without permission.

Legal Disclaimer

The author and the publisher of this work have made every effort to ensure the accuracy of information contained within at the time of publication and shall have no liability or responsibility to any person, or entity for any losses or damages incurred, or alleged to have been incurred directly or indirectly by the information contained in this book. The author or publisher make no warranties, expressed or implied, with respect to its content and no warranties may be created or extended by sales representatives, or written sales materials. The author or publisher have no responsibility for the consistency or accuracy of URLs and content of third-party websites referenced in this book. The author and publisher recommend that the reader always consult current regulations, applicable research, and institutional policy and procedures.

The publisher and the author make no guarantees concerning the level of success you may experience by following the advice and strategies contained in this book, and you accept the risk that results will differ for each individual. The testimonials and examples provided in this book show exceptional results, which may not apply to the average reader and are not intended to represent or guarantee that you will achieve the same or similar results.

The publisher and the author do not make any guarantee or other promise as to any results that may be obtained from using the content of this book. You should never make any investment decision without first consulting with your own financial advisor and conducting your own research and due diligence. To the maximum extent permitted by law, the publisher and the author disclaim any and all liability in the event any information, commentary, analysis, opinions, advice and/or recommendations contained in this book prove to be inaccurate, incomplete or unreliable, or result in any investment or other losses.

Cover Copy by Blurb Writer.com

This book is dedicated to a great bunch - Patty
Andrews, Lisa Weber, Cindi Ghosh, Marie Hemeon,
Melissa Prouty, Phyllis Tarbell, Shannon Tatro, Colleen
Moore, Mary Driscoll, Laura Lamarre, Patty Squiers,
Mary Pleasant and Marie Hoffman.
In memory of Cindy Tilley, Anne Hill and Kathy
Miottke.

Introduction to The Clinical Manager Source

Developed as a way to meet the needs of new and current Clinical Managers in the Home Health and Hospice space; The Clinical Manager Source http://th eclinicalmanagersource.com offers newsletters, courses, podcasts and books like these. Visit us online!

CONTENTS

Chapter One

INTRODUCTION

T hank you for picking up this book! Before you settle in and get reading, I wanted to let you know why I wrote it. I've spent nearly thirty years working in the home health and hospice industry, and I've spent the same amount of time remarking on the lack of resources and training needed for clinical managers. So many times, I've seen agencies promote wonderful nurses and clinicians who excel at clinical work into management positions, with little or no training in how to do their jobs. Then they wonder why they are failing or are not getting the expected results from such a good clinician.

I was one of those nurses many moons ago, and I struggled to get it right. Eventually, it all came together, because of my perseverance, sheer will and a little luck. But it wasn't without fall-out for my lack of knowledge and skill. My lack of expertise and immature management and leadership skills affected the people I supervised and the agency where I worked.

Things could have been different. They could have gone more smoothly, and I could have had less anxiety and stress throughout the process. While I did eventually figure it out, it was not without pain and a lot of trial and error. My lack of 'know-how' no doubt did damage. My experience was a long time ago. What's surprising is that this is still happening today.

In my career, I have worked in most of the positions available in a home health and hospice agency for a nurse. I also eventually became the CEO of the agency where I started out as a visiting nurse after working in acute care for a few years. During that time, we merged the agency into the local health system, and my title changed to Executive Director, where I reported to the hospital's CEO. While the title changed, the job was the same. I was part of the executive team for the health system for 10 years before I became a consultant with the largest, most tenured home health and hospice firm in the country. In that role over the past 15 years, I worked with home health and hospice clients in 48 states. I just missed out on stepping foot in Wyoming and North Dakota.

In those 15 years, I worked with hundreds of clinical managers and have seen firsthand the lack of education and resources for the role of the clinical manager, specifically as it pertains to the home health and hospice arenas. There are clinical, regulatory and management resources out there, but very few that cater directly to the home health or hospice clinical manager.

This has always seemed crazy to me. Every agency depends on what happens (or doesn't) in the clinical manager role. The quality of clinical care, regulatory compliance, utilization and financial management are among some aspects that clinical managers directly control. Lack of knowledge in any of these aspects can derail the success of the entire organization.

I have heard from owners, CEOs and CFOs throughout the US say countless times, "if the clinical managers would just do.... (BLANK) everything would be great." But few have actually taken the time or provided the resources to make sure their clinical managers are knowledgeable in all the areas they have responsibility and influence.

Part of the problem is that there is not a single resource out there that helps the home health or hospice clinical manager translate all the information into how best to do their job in practice. You can find out the best wound care, read up on regulations and understand reimbursement—but there is limited information available to guide clinical managers in how best to assimilate and apply that information into doing the job. That is why, now semi-retired in 2022, I created this book along with other resources specifically designed for clinical managers in the home health and hospice space.

At **theclinicalmanagersource.com** there are courses, a newsletter, podcasts and written materials specifically for these roles. My goal is to provide easy to access and less expensive resources that are geared towards really busy people with a limited amount of time on their hands.

This book has an accompanying workbook available geared towards self-guided planning for future education and personal career growth goal setting. Using it will help you focus on the key aspects of the book and to develop your personal growth plan.

Chapter Two

THE ROLE TODAY

The job of the clinical manager in home health or hospice is not for the fainthearted. It's a difficult but necessary role in any agency. Today and into the future, there are many factors at play that influence the challenges that this role must grapple with on a daily basis. There are staffing challenges where there are just not enough nurses to care for the patients, which can make scheduling nearly an art form. There are regulatory challenges with heightened scrutiny of surveys and documentation reviewed at several junctions prior to determining whether Medicare (CMS) will pay the agency for the services rendered. Finally, let's not forget the narrow financial margins agencies face in the first place!

The clinical manager balances all these priorities from moment to moment on a daily basis in order to ensure care is delivered to the patients on their team. The quality of the clinical care, the adherence to regulation, the utilization of resources and the needs of the employees are all balanced by the clinical manager. Failure or dereliction of duty in any area could have a devastating effect on the entire organization.

The value of this critical position is apparent in many organizations. Currently across the country, there are open positions offering huge, unprecedented hiring bonuses for clinical manager roles. The need to fill vacancies is there, and agencies may recognize the value of the role. However, many organizations cannot train, nurture, or grow the persons in these roles. Once filled, either by hiring or promoting a staff member into the role, there is no further activity to support their overall success.

Many agencies will look internally to promote 'good clinicians' into manager positions. They assume that the clinical performance and skill will translate into a high functioning clinical manager. Nothing could be farther from the truth. Orientation and mentorship programs, while full of good intention, often lack the substance needed to train a new manager. Mentorships often fail, not because of a lack of desire, but because of a lack of time. Asking a very busy clinical manager to mentor a new one on another team is an enormous challenge. Meeting and getting together away from the busyness and needs of the teams can prove impossible. Often, these programs lack a proper direction or purpose. Without goals and oversight, the overall intent is unmet.

Completing a checklist and a video on how to manage difficult people are the standard few days plan for orientations I have seen for clinical managers. This is not just something in the home health or hospice services but is reported in other areas of health care as well, even in countries with more organized, socialized medicine. The role of the clinical manager is the lynchpin for success of the organization, and largely, health care organizations have failed to train and adequately grow the role.

A clinical manager needs to have the knowledge and skill set to apply to competently navigate through the five core areas of home health and hospice. These five areas are the pillars for the success for the clinical manager. Deficits in any of these areas will have a detrimental impact on the overall organization.

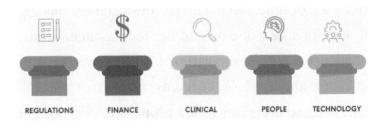

In this book, you will learn the basics in all five areas and the overall functions of each area, and typical processes followed by successful agencies. You will learn the best practices to apply your knowledge to these areas. You will end the book with an understanding of what your particular needs are and where you need to focus your time and energy to improve. Optionally, you can work along with the companion workbook and/or courses available on the website, www.theclinicalmanagersource.com.

The Role of the Clinical Manager

The role that the clinical manager in Home Health fulfills is essentially the same when comparing the small agency to the larger agency. Often, the smaller the agency, the larger the span of responsibility of the clinical manager, managing everything from intake to quality. The overall role is one of great importance to the agency. It's what happens between the clinical manager and their staff that moves the agency forward. I like to refer to the job as being the linchpin of the agency. The linchpin is the very important piece of sturdy metal that holds the wheels on a vehicle. If the linchpin breaks or is otherwise faulty, the wheel falls off and the entire operation can come off the rails. The analogy holds true in the role of clinical manager. If it's not working right, there are bound to be problems!

The Job Description

A phrase comes to mind, "Chief, Cook and Bottle washer," meaning that this person is in charge of all vital but routine responsibilities in the organization. Everything that must happen in the agency happens at the hands of the clinical manager. Clinical, financial, human resources, customer service and regulatory management encompass this role. Below is a common listing of what the industry typically includes in the job description for the role of clinical manager.

- Directs, coordinates and evaluates the delivery of home health services to a team of patients ensuring compliance with agency policy, and State and Federal Regulations.

- Oversees the clinical care provided by direct reports, ensuring competencies and appropriate care.

- Oversees the utilization of services provided, working with the clinical team to ensure the plan of care meets patient needs.

- Manages staffing levels, ensuring adequate staffing levels.

- Makes in home supervisory visits to the clinical staff.

- Oversees the scheduling of clinical services, ensuring coverage of patient care needs on a 24/7 basis.

- Works with human resources to recruit, hire and train clinical staff. Works to ensure an environment conducive to employee retention.

- Manages staff assignments, overall caseloads and monitors team and individual productivity.

- Reviews documentation to ensure OASIS, plan of care and ICD-10 are completed accurately. May work with outsourced coding/OASIS review services or internal review teams to ensure direct reports documentation is completed accurately and timely.

- Conducts team and individual caseload reviews and case conferences with assigned teams on a regularly scheduled basis to ensure quality outcomes are met.

- Works with the quality and compliance teams to ensure regulations, standards and quality outcome goals are met. Takes part in survey preparation for state, federal, and accreditation surveys.

- Works with the finance department to ensure documentation is in place for billing. Collaborates with finance on budgets and financial targets.

- Represents the agency in the community and on requested committees with other health care groups, health system or professional organizations.

- Is a role model and a mentor for assigned staff in meeting the organizational goals.

- Takes supervisory/administrative on call.

- Makes visits as a nurse in low staffing situations.

Place in the organization

As we study the context of the clinical manager role, we should look at where it sits in the organization and what processes depend on the function of the clinical team. For example, the agency will not meet the quality outcome targets unless the clinical manager teaches, reinforces and monitors the quality of care with their staff. This is done by hiring experienced clinicians, ensuring they meet the competence standards for the organization, reviewing plans of care and performing case reviews to ensure that the plan of care meets the needs of the patient and will move them to improve.

An additional example is in finance, the agency will not be financially successful unless the clinical manager is actively managing the staff's productivity (budgets) and staff are completing their paperwork in a timely manner (billing and revenue cycle).

The following chart depicts all the organizational functions that depend on the role of clinical manager to process, oversee, and essentially move things forward.

Larger home health agencies with several clinical teams will have a clinical manager assigned to each team relative to its size. Smaller agencies will often have the clinical manager take on roles of quality and/or intake along with the clinical manager role, because of a smaller patient census. The following is a chart which depicts where the clinical manager role typically sits in an organization.

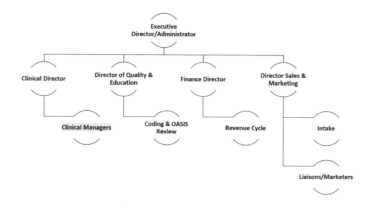

What Makes A Good Clinical Manager?

What is the secret sauce that creates a good clinical manager? Being responsible for so many things all at once can be daunting and overwhelming for many people. But there are those who make it through their day and do it well, meeting all the needs of their staff, patients and internal customers. With so much on the plate for this role, how are they able to do it?

There are a set of qualities that work well in the overall role and some that are essential to being successful. Before I get to filling in a list of adjectives for the ideal clinical manager, I want you to think about the manager that most influenced you. I am sure that you could describe what made that manager stand out in your view. What were those qualities?

For me, one clinical manager I had years ago still stands out in my mind as a superb manager. Still, to this day, her qualities are what I look for when hiring or coaching and strive to continue to emulate in my own life.

Likeable and fair—was personable. Set out the rules for the team, but also upheld them herself. Did not have any perceived 'favorites', treated everyone to the same standards.

Would roll up her sleeves and help. Was an excellent clinician and respected by physicians and other managers. When things got busy or I needed a hand with a procedure that I was unfamiliar with or not skilled at—she jumped in and helped me and others.

Knew her stuff—I would think of this as a sub-quality for rolling up her sleeves—but I knew I could rely on her to know what to do or to direct me to the resources I needed.

Trusted the team—We could self-schedule, but the calendar had to have a minimum coverage each day, including weekends and holidays. It always worked. We knew we had to fill it in and had a responsibility to the team and the patients. We could schedule to fit in our lives, but we had to balance that with the needs of the agency.

In my career, I have always tried to emulate the behavior of those managers I worked with that were effective. Knowing what worked for you as a team member in relation to your managers can really help to structure your own behavior as you grow in your career. I want to emphasize that point: evolution. We are always learning and developing as human beings, and we should be doing the same for our work. As clinicians, we are always learning new things and applying them. As a clinical manager, it should be the same. Learning and growing helps you to be a better manager and to be more successful.

If you have the workbook, you can follow along by listing out those areas you admire in your own previous experiences with past managers you have worked for. If you don't have the workbook, please still make a list of those qualities. The list will come into play at the end of the book/workbook where we develop your own work plan, outlining your steps to be more successful in the role of clinical manager.

Your Own Strengths and Weaknesses

Part of learning and growth is to identify where your strengths and weaknesses lie. There is not a test or a grade at the end of this book. You won't be judged by what you identify or what you don't. It's about your own growth. As you move through the chapters and topics, identify areas you feel the need to grow with. These areas need to go into your overall growth plan.

I always need to grow in the financial realms. This was not my natural habitat as a nurse, and so I find I needed to grow in these areas all the time. The tie between clinical and financial work makes for the success or failure of the home health agency, and so it was always important to understand the payment systems and the overall impact on the agency. Most importantly, was the translation of what to do with that knowledge, and how to apply it to my daily life of coaching the clinical team.

With the clinical manager's job having such an enormous expanse of responsibility, I can't imagine anyone that doesn't have something on their work plan. The fact that you've picked up this book, shows you are willing to grow and learn!

In your notes or in the workbook, make yourself a note on where you would like to enhance your knowledge base. While it may not be apparent right now, as you read further, you may identify more areas to refine your skill set.

Chapter Three

PILLAR #1: REGULATIONS

REGULATIONS

I want to start out this chapter by emphasizing that there are A LOT of regulations in the home health and hospice industry. And when I say that, I really mean it. There are so many, and they seem to change frequently. There are different nuances and interpretations that throw uncertainty into the mix. The BEST advice I can give you is to make sure you have good references. Going right to the source is always the best bet. This means that you should keep links on your computer desktop to all the regulations inclusive of both state and federal, to the Centers for Medicare and Medicaid Services (CMS) and to your state association. This ensures that you have access to the most accurate and up-to-date sources when you need them. The archaic practice of printing out the regulations to keep in binders in your office is really obsolete. It doesn't ensure that you can keep up to date with changes and updates, and it takes up space and collects dust. Not to mention that it wastes paper, ink and energy creating all of those dusty binders.

Since there are so many regulations in this industry, you need to accept that you can't remember them all, let alone all the details. Having a quick digital reference is the best way to ensure that you are referring to the most current information. ALSO, I want to point out that even experts with years and years of experience still reference the rules. I look at them several times a week, to refer to something a client has asked me or to refresh my memory on a particular aspect. I email folks I know and work with occasionally to ask the "am I crazy" questions about rules and regulations and they email me with the same questions. And I'm an expert, as are the people that I ask.

Please get into the habit of looking things up when you feel you need to. No one is perfect and no one I know can recite chapter and verse of the regulations. (Well, maybe one or two people...) Looking things up is a strength, not a weakness!

In the resources section at the back of the book, there is a list of links for you to refer to. Save them to your desktop on your computer, not on your actual desktop next to your pencils and your houseplants. Put them some place you will remember to look for them.

I also want to be clear that this book is not a book on the regulations. We don't have the time or the space. I'll give a high-level overview of what a clinical manager should know. It's your responsibility to know the rules that apply to your role. There are a lot of free resources out there to refresh and update your knowledge of the rules. Knowing the regulations will take up a lot of your time as a clinical manager both now and in the future. As they change or get updated, you'll have to learn new things. Having been around as long as I have, I have seen a lot of updates and tweaks to rules and regulations. Just realize you'll be learning and updating forever along with the rest of the industry.

The Beginning – How a Home Health Agency Starts Up

To make things a little less confusing, let's consider a home health agency that wants to start up services. First, the owners–whether it be an entrepreneur or a health system–have to consider the time and cost associated with this process. It can take up to two years sometimes to get all the approvals to even bill for the care provided. And these payments are not retroactive to when you first began to see patients, only back to your approval date. This means you have to have a functioning agency, with patients and staff, before money comes in the door. It's not an endeavor for the fainthearted or those without financial resources.

Certificate of Need

The agency needs to first comply with the Certificate of Need (CON) regulations in the state they want to provide services. This means that the aspiring owners need to get approval from the state to open and run a home health agency by proving there is a need for the care in the area. Not all states have this requirement, but many do. It controls the numbers of providers in an area, and by doing so, they supposedly control the costs of health care.

To add to this, the new owners would also want to do a further needs assessment in the area they are planning on servicing. While they do this for the CON, if applicable, there are other nuances to consider. A lot of areas in the country have multiple home health or hospice providers, creating fierce competition not only for patients, but for staff. This is definitely a consideration in reviewing the potential for success in an area.

State Regulations

Some states will have their own specific home health or hospice regulations and licensure. This means that the home health agency must follow those rules, along with the federal rules. As a first step in the certification process for a new agency–state licensure is it. There is usually an application process, approval and then an on-site survey prior to the agency getting the okay to take patients. Overall, these rules usually closely follow the federal regulations.

Some states will have regulations that differ from the federal rules. The agency must follow the strictest rule. For example, the state of CT has specific staffing ratios for clinical managers. These outline how many direct care professional staff a clinical manager can oversee. Although this is not part of the federal rules, every home health agency in CT must follow these stricter rules.

Another example is in NJ, there is a requirement in the state regulations that a home health clinical manager have a BSN degree. This is not required in the federal regulations, but every home health agency in NJ needs to follow the same rule with their clinical managers, all having the BS degree.

State regulations are usually online at the licensing and certification sites, health care or the state's Department of Public Health. Each state handles licensing requirements differently. Make sure you know where to find your state rules and save that link to your desktop along with the federal rules.

Medicare Rules

Medicare–CMS–has specific rules that a home health agency must follow in order to be certified under the Medicare program to provide care to Medicare beneficiaries and to be paid by the program. These are the Conditions of Participation (CoPs). These rules include everything from the overall structure of the organization to the education and training of staff roles, to the content of the plan of care for a patient. We have to follow these rules in order to get reimbursed by Medicare. Every home health agency must follow these same rules. The COPs are outlined in the Code of Federal Regulations (CFR).

The conditions that home health agencies must follow are essentially laws. These are decided upon by Congress and published in the Federal Register. Updates and changes are usually published in the Federal Register. Usually in home health, we see proposed rules changes published in the summer roughly within the May–July timeframe. While the Final Rules are published in the fall for an effective date of October 1 (which is the federal fiscal calendar) or January 1st effective date. I love to read the Federal Register publication of rules because you do find out a lot. Often there are long pre-ambles to explain the Centers for Medicare/Medicaid Services (CMS's) process and thinking, as well as comments from providers and responses from the government. Sometime when you have the chance to do so, read it! You'll find it to be very educational.

The government outlines further rule-making in the manuals CMS publishes. For home health, these manuals are the Benefit Policy Manual Chapter 7 and the Home Health Claims processing Manual Chapter 10. Both are located at the Home Health Center on the CMS website. Another significant reason to not print these manuals out is that these are updated frequently. When you click the links, you will see the date that the manual was updated and, for a time, they will keep the updates colored in red, making them easy to see. (See the links in the Resources section of this book).

There is a lot of information in these manuals, and I urge you to read through them periodically. It will give you a great foundation and comprehension to heed this advice. They're a great resource, as mentioned earlier, and they can help to explain why things are done the way they are in your agency. Every home health agency across the country has to follow the same set of rules. Most are functioning in the same way, with similar structures and processes. There are nuances, of course, particularly with state rules and accreditation bodies.

Medicare Certification

Now, in order to bill and be a Medicare certified agency, that agency will need to undergo an on-site survey. The aspiring owner will have sent their application to be a Medicare provider to the regional office and triggered this review. There are interpretive guidelines that the surveyors follow which provide guidance on meeting the COP requirements. These are helpful to know for the clinical manager, providing insight into how the rules should be applied. The link is provided at the end of the book in the Resources section.

You should know that most states are not providing new agencies with the initial survey for Medicare certification. They have too much to do to keep up with the routine surveys and complaint surveys of all the providers in their state to accommodate adding one more.

Deemed Status

The unavailability of surveyors for initial certifications has created the need for new agencies to undergo a Deemed Status Survey. The process involves meeting the standards for the accreditation body, along with the Medicare COPs in order to become Medicare certified. By meeting both the accreditation standards and the COPs, the agency is granted deemed status. This means they must undergo accreditation through the Joint Commission (JC or JCAHO), the Accreditation Commission for Health Care (ACHC), or the Community Health Accreditation Partnership (CHAP). The written standards are available from the accrediting agency, the agency should obtain these as part of the arrangement to be accredited.

There is a charge of several thousand dollars for this survey, but for many agencies wanting to start up as a home health agency, this is the only way they can get Medicare certification. After a round, or several rounds of paperwork including the accreditation body notifying Medicare of the survey results, the agency is then given a provider number and the ability to bill for services once finally approved.

So now consider if your agency has an accreditation, you will be bound to follow the accreditation standards, the federal COPs, and your state rules if applicable. Feels like a lot of rules, right? Now I hope you see why I recommend that you keep these rules at your fingertips, and reference them frequently.

Additional Rules

Home health agencies are also bound to the Outcome Assessment and Information Set (OASIS) regulations. The OASIS is a mandated assessment with pre-scripted questions for clinicians to complete at specific intervals (admission, discharge, transfer, resumption, recertification, and death). These are the requirement to gather and submit patient data from specific mandated OASIS questions. Gathered at specific time points, the data is transmitted to a repository and used for both payment and quality data. Agencies that do not submit their data have a 2% payment penalty for all their home health episodes. This means Medicare will reduce all reimbursement by 2%. There are specific rules and guidance for the use of the OASIS data set.

HIPAA, the set of regulations that exists to protect the privacy of patients, provides confidentiality and security standards, and protects the medical records of people being served by the health system from having their personal medical information shared without their permission. These are another set of regulations that home health agencies are bound to follow. The privacy and security components are vital for the home health clinical manager to know. The sharing of information and keeping records secure are paramount in our industry, as we are out and about in the community and have paper and electronic devices that can be stolen.

International Classification of Disease (ICD 10) coding guidelines are required by the HIPAA rules. These rules provide guidelines for the accuracy of diagnosis coding. Since these rules drive payments in home health, as part of the payment calculation, accuracy is vital.

Agency Policy and Procedure

Every agency is required to have specific policies and procedures in place as part of the certification and accreditation processes. These include everything from the admission and discharge of patients to personnel requirements and clinical procedures. A lot of agencies will purchase a policy and procedure manual and edit it to match the home health agency's name and practices. Many agencies will also purchase a clinical procedure manual for their staff to reference. Preferably, this procedure manual reflects the home setting.

These policies and procedures become the rules for your agency. This is another set of rules that you will need to know and reference in order to do your job. A home health agency's policies will be referenced by surveyors. So, if you are not following your own policies, you may end up with a citation on a survey.

Quality and Performance Improvement

Two other areas in which you will need to have a handle on are quality and compliance. I bundled these areas under regulation because, as a clinical manager, day-to-day operations can blend these areas for you, instead of being a separate force and departments in your agency. "Quality" in a home health agency usually refers to clinical outcomes and performance improvement. Agencies are required to have formal Quality Assessment and Performance Improvement (QAPI) activities occurring in their agencies. This means that there is activity to discover opportunities for improvement, such as in data collection and review or record audits to ensure specific tasks and best practices are being followed.

A home health agencies' clinical outcome, as collected in the OASIS assessments, is publicly available and published on the web. The *Compare* website provides comparisons of healthcare providers—hospitals, nursing homes, home health, and hospice agencies. Data is available for comparison and review by anyone in the country. Looking to measure your agency against another or select care options for a parent? This is a good resource.

Some data that is publicly reported is from the agency claims data. This makes it 'cleaner' in that there are not nuances related to the accuracy of the OASIS. It simply reflects where a patient received care–such as being transferred to a hospital or using an ER.

Home health agencies are also required to have patient satisfaction data publicly reported. All agencies across the country are measured by the same publicly reported questions. Agencies will often have other questions depending on their vendor that they collect data.

With all the data available for QAPI, agencies can focus on specific areas to improve their overall performance. Invariably, as a clinical manager, you may be involved in these activities. Analyzing the data to understand why the results are not as good as other agencies can reveal issues that you can assist in rectifying. Changing approaches to care or education of clinicians often drive the improvement in performance.

I always like to say that we need to ask the data what it's telling us, in order to understand the problem that needs to be fixed. Often the initial data point, such as high ER use, is not the only information you need to resolve the issue. Digging in further, such as the time of day or day of week, that patients are using the ER will help to tell the full story. Identifying specific reasons for the ER visit, such as diagnosis, co-morbidities and situations, can reveal a lot. Performance improvement can be a lot of fun for the clinical manager, shedding light on areas for improvement and offering the opportunity to be the best in your service area at a particular aspect of care.

Some payors look to contract with home health agencies that have good performance measures and can prove that the care they provide will save money by not sending patients to the ER or being re-hospitalized. It's easy to compare agencies by looking online. Medicare/CMS is also looking to save money with good performing agencies. Value-Based Purchasing (VBP), which had been a pilot program in nine states for the past five years, is now going to come to all home health agencies across the country beginning in 2023. This means that there will be a bonus, or a penalty based on the agency's performance in specific outcome measures. The payment bump or penalty will be 5% upside or downside. Consider that 5% of a $2,500 30-day period is $125. Multiply that by how many periods your agency has, and that's some serious cash. And that's right you've got it, CMS is looking to remove the poor players from the mix. Purchasing services that provide value to the Medicare pocketbook is their goal.

Compliance

Compliance is one of those areas that can mean a lot of different things to a lot of different people. Many agencies consider compliance with the survey and certification rules as their compliance. Some agencies view compliance as intertwined with quality or performance improvement. When I refer to compliance, largely, I mean compliance with the conditions of payment, the rules that must be followed in order for Medicare to pay an agency. Larger agencies will usually separate these activities in their review and oversight, while smaller agencies combine the activities.

My personal experience working with agencies is that the conditions of participation and the conditions of payment are often confused. I have been at agencies and shown them issues with certifications or orders management that affect their payment, and they were shocked there is a problem because a surveyor was just on-site, and they had passed with flying colors. It's important to understand the differences and areas where you may have a risk that you can influence or control as a clinical manager. Because the fact is, you can have a great survey–but if your documentation is lacking to support skill or homebound or MD orders are not back signed–your payment is at risk.

Some areas for home health conditions of payment include:

- Signed and dated consents.

- Signed and dated plan of care (485) (certified to the 5 requirements–homebound, under care of MD, POC, F2F, skilled need..

- Signed and dated orders for all services, frequency, modality and duration.

- Face to face by the allowed provider, in the allowed timeframe, for the reasons referred to home health.

- Skilled & Medically Necessary services supported in documentation, signed and dated by clinician (nursing, therapy).

- Homebound supported in documentation.

- If therapy is provided, supervisions are done every 30 days by each discipline.

A lightbulb should go off in your mind as you review this list. These are the targeted areas important in reviews at agencies. If problems exist in these areas, then they need to be resolved in order for the agency to be paid. You may find revenue cycle staff at your door looking for help in getting documents signed, visits completed or various other things that are holding up billing.

Other areas of compliance that you need to be aware of are claim denials and particular reviews by Medicare or its contractors. Periodically, CMS, through its regional contractors, will perform audits. There may be a particular trigger in which they are reviewing, such as therapy utilization or other areas in which your agency may be an outlier. Agencies can view their Program for Evaluating Payment Patterns Electronic Report (PEP-PER) provided periodically to review the areas that are being scrutinized and seen as high risk. CMS can use this data and other probes to assess compliance. As we don't submit the full records to Medicare prior to being paid, these periodic reviews help assess whether an agency complies with the Medicare rules. These typically come as an Additional Document Request (ADR) and are requested via the billing system, or rarely, sent in the mail. The agency will have a set timeframe to send the patient chart information in for review. The claims will be on hold until the review is completed if it's a pre-payment review. The claims will be cleared once approved, however you will find out if you have claim denials in the same manner.

Denials are a problem. They need to be reviewed and appealed if possible. As a clinical manager, you may be involved in this process, depending on the size of your agency. They are a problem, because they can trigger further reviews. There are several areas of focus for home health and hospice agencies that trigger larger reviews. (There is a listing in the Resources chapter under Palmetto.)

Program integrity contractors are the auditors that work with Medicare to ensure that agencies are following the conditions of participation and of payment. These include the Medicare Administrative Contractors (MACs), Recovery Audit Contractors (RACs), the Unified Program Integrity Contractors (UPICs) the Zone Program Integrity Contractors (ZPICs) and the Medicaid Integrity Contractors (MICs).

If your agency is an outlier in any areas, such as in the PEPPER report, you can expect to have periodic ADRs to "test" whether you are following the rules and your documentation is good enough to be paid. Also, if you have claim denials during any of these probes, they can refer you for more intense review. The concern is that on some reviews, the UPIC typically, if they pull records and find you have x% of claims that are denied, they can extrapolate that percentage to the agency's universe of claims. That can mean big dollar paybacks for agencies. So, you see why good documentation and knowing the rules for payment can help to reduce the risk that any home health agency faces.

I've listed further resources at the end of this book if you are interested in delving deeper into the areas of risk management for home health and compliance. It's fascinating stuff!

Credentialing of Staff

A few other areas a clinical manager should know about in the credentialing of staff. All the professional staff need to be licensed as required by your state and the COPs. While this is a Human Resource/People topic, it is also a compliance topic. While it would violate the state nursing practice to have a nurse caring for patients with an expired license, it could also prohibit you from billing for those visits as a nursing visit. It's not just an HR headache when you have a staff member forgetting to renew their license–it can be a compliance/billing nightmare. This would be the same as physicians signing orders who are not physicians, have no license or aren't enrolled in Provider, Enrollment, Chain and Ownership System (PECOS). The agency could not bill for those services. Ensure your agency has a process for credential employees and physicians to ensure licensure and PECOS enrollment.

Also, as part of the credentialing of employees and signing providers, there needs to be a verification step of ensuring these individuals are not on the Office of Inspector General's (OIG) exclusion list. The OIG has a listing that is maintained for individuals that have committed some type of fraud and are now excluded from the Medicare program. Similar to doing visits without a license, if your staff are on the exclusion list, you cannot bill Medicare for these services. Keep in mind it can be anyone–even aides on this list. Make sure someone in your agency is checking this on hire and periodically thereafter.

To stay on top of what the OIG is focusing on, you can sign up to receive their daily emails about their enforcement action. Home health and hospice agencies will sometimes appear there, so it makes interesting reading.

Best Practices

So now you're prepared with the regulations. You've got them all saved electronically to your desktop.

You've read through them and reference them period-ically. But where is the sweet spot of knowledge for a clinical manager in being an expert with the reg-ulations? That's a good question! Ideally, you should know and follow the rules expertly. However, there are specific things you need to be an expert in as a clinical manager, which you will use day to day guiding and coaching your team.

The first is in the overall patient care arena. What are the qualifications for a patient in home health? Refer to the Medicare Benefit Policy Manual Chapter 7.

- Must be under the care of a MD or allowed practitioner.

- Must be homebound.

- Has a plan of care established and periodically reviewed by a MD or allowed practitioner.

- Has a skilled intermittent nursing need, or PT, ST or continuing need for OT.

- Be certified to all the above by their MD or allowed practitioner–AND have had a face to face in the allowed time frame.

As a clinical manager, you will deal with these five things all day, every day. Mostly, you will focus on the 'homebound' and 'skilled' requirements. These can be a challenge for a clinical manager because you must review the cases with staff and are reliant on their accurate communication and from documentation in the record of what is happening in the home. This is the reason the case review is so valuable. It allows for the clinicians to report on why the patient is homebound or skilled and what the plan is for continuing care. It's that day-to-day teaching and review of cases with your clinical team that ensures compliance with the regulations, and allows for oversight of patient care and staff knowledge of the regulations.

The skilled and homebound criteria should be part of the overall orientation of new staff, as well as part of the ongoing training and annual competencies. Reviewing and discussing these areas are important. It helps in keeping these requirements at the top of everyone's mind. They can't be heard enough.

Reviewing clinical record documentation is vital. Remember the adage, "if it's not documented, it's not done". Review your staff's documentation continually. You can do this while looking at caseloads and performing case reviews. Pull up those patient records, and look at what staff are documenting for homebound and skill while they talk to you. If your organization requires you to complete a set of audits, make sure they include this information in the review process. Educate staff continuously about these requirements and how they apply to their patients. This is such a vital aspect of your role as a clinical manager. Your attention will ensure compliance and protect reimbursement.

Another vital role of the clinical manager is to ensure your working knowledge of the survey process. A survey can occur any day in a home health agency, and the best way to ensure passing is to always be prepared. Focusing on compliance with the regulations should not be only when you expect a surveyor to walk through the door, it should be an ongoing process. The intent of the regulations is that all the agencies follow them, ensuring that the quality of care is good and payment is fair. Regulations are considered the minimum standard. They should be followed routinely.

Incorporating the elements that a surveyor would assess when you perform in home supervisory visits with your staff can help to assure compliance as well. Make sure staff understands the regulations and policies such as bag technique and infection control during the home visit. Ensure orders and plans of care are in place, and that they communicate changes to the physician or allowed provider who is overseeing the plan of care.

In the day to day of the clinical manager, you will reference a lot of regulations. You will need to ensure that the correct disciplines are admitting the patient in a staffing crunch, or the correct timing of the OASIS is being completed for a patient with a recertification and resumption of care at the same time or strategizing what to do with a patient who doesn't have a community physician.

Knowing the regulations and creating a solid foundation for yourself is vital. No matter where you go in your career, the regulations will follow. It may seem daunting, but take it a step at a time. Where do you need reinforcement? What regulations perplex you?

My advice is to start with the Conditions of Participation. Review them and make notes where you have questions and what you want to follow-up with. After that, review the interpretive guidelines, and then the Medicare Manuals—Chapter 7 and Chapter 10. Follow the same process for taking notes.

I read them and review them periodically on my own, regardless of who I am working on or what project I'm doing. Personally, I like to keep fresh as long as I am still active in the industry. I also read the rule-making that comes out in the summer as proposed rules, and the final rules that come out in the fall. It's interesting to gain insight into the full text. Don't worry, it's not totally boring, it really applies to what you do on a day-to-day basis. It can be eye opening to read.

Set a goal to make the regulations a priority. It's one of the pillars I've established for the role of the clinical manager. Again, I will reiterate that it is a strength to rely on resources, going right to the source for the regulation. Put those links on your computer desktop and have a bonfire with those dusty outdated binders!

Chapter Four

PILLAR #2: FINANCE

FINANCE

So... okay, I hear you on the timing of the last two chapters, regulations and finance. One right after the other! It's some pretty heavy material, I get it! But remember, these are the pillars of knowledge that you need to have a handle on to be successful as a manager in the industry. I can honestly say that the area of finance was not one of my strengths when I started into clinical management. I made a lot of mistakes because of that lack of knowledge, and I want you to avoid making those same types of mistakes.

Many folks in clinical management or leadership positions struggle with finance and it raises the stress level of everyone when we talk about money. Largely, the stress comes from feeling inadequate or solid in understanding the ins and outs of finance. I want to help fix that for you, reduce your stress by building a foundation of knowledge you can build on. Understand that your agency, whether it be a for profit privately owned, publicly traded or a non-profit VNA, needs to have money coming in the door in order to function. Whether we like it, or not, we are working at a business with taxes to pay and payroll to meet. Our success or failure in managing the money at our agency drives whether we can stay in business. This is like our own personal finances. If we have money coming in, we can afford our mortgage or rent. If we don't, we are sleeping on the couch at a friend's house. The goal for money management, of course, is to have enough left over to focus on growth or new technology. Similar to our personal lives, where we strive to have enough left over for vacations to Disney World or other goals.

Revenue

Every organization has revenue and expenses. *Revenue* is essentially the money that is coming in the door from claims. Most home health and hospice agencies' revenue comes from the services provided. This is Medicare, or Managed Medicare, commercial insurance under private or employer plans, or Medicaid, or Managed Medicaid. The actual sources of revenue for each agency can vary and will vary widely from state to region the agency serves. Because the revenue is coming from services (nursing, therapy, social work, aide etc.) that the agency provides to people, the insurance coverage of the people served is reflected in the *revenue* for the agency. This would be what the insurance plans will pay for services.

For example, I was once the Executive Director of a VNA & Hospice that provided services to a lower socio-economic county in the state. Much of our revenue was from Medicaid, in fact, we were 50% Medicaid. In the town north of my agency, which was more affluent, the VNA there had a 15% Medicaid revenue. The *payor mix*, the different payors in the revenue, differs from town to town and region to region. Payors are different insurance companies, federal or state programs that pay for services in the home.

Payor Mix

Payor Mix has a lot of influence on the agency in how the agency needs to manage to be successful. This is important to note. Because like it or not, how we get paid in healthcare has an influence on how care is delivered. That is an honest truth. Back in olden times in home health (when I first started), Medicare reimbursed the home health on a per visit basis. Being paid without pre-approvals or authorizations was freeing. We provided more visits without worrying about reimbursement. It created a dependency factor as well. Patients were more reliant on the agency and less self-reliant. Outcomes weren't a consideration, and utilization was high. That changed with the Prospective Payment System (PPS) in 2000, where care moved from being per visit to being reimbursed episodically, payment was based on a 60-day episode of care. This was further refined in recent years by the Patient Driven Groupings Model (PDGM), where payment was further changed to 30-day periods.

The payor mix at your agency will differ from other agencies. Particularly if you consider looking at different regions of the country. Some places will have more Managed Medicare, where the seniors in the area the agency serves have selected a Managed Medicare product instead of the traditional Medicare coverage. Note that they are not all the same either from locale to locale, some will require prior authorization, and some will pay on a per visit basis instead of episodically. A lot of managed care products influence the utilization of services by having an authorization process, initial or ongoing. Some can be more restrictive than others. Your agency's contracts with insurance companies may also vary for payment, with some being less than Medicare reimbursement.

It is good to know the payor mix at your organization. Do you have a lot of traditional Medicare, or do you have a lot of Managed Products and Medicaid? If you know this information, it will help understand the drivers of your particular agency. Remember that every agency has to follow the same federal regulations, with nuances for state and accreditation, but not every agency has the same payor mix drivers. This is important to note where you work as a clinical manager, it will help to align the need to balance the revenue with the expenses.

Operating Revenue

If you get to see financial statements for your agency, sometimes you will see different ways that they split the revenue up. Typically, most organizations will have operating revenue and non-operating revenue. Each organization is unique in how they report and display revenue, so keep that in mind.

Operating revenue refers to the money that is received for the services provided. This includes all the payors and all the services billed. Organizations can further break this down by payor and by program. Some really progressive agencies will break these numbers down further to match reporting structures, and can report revenue and expense by program, branch and team. Operating revenue is the area that clinical managers live under. This is where the clinical manager has direct influence, by assisting the team to manage utilization, get authorizations, and complete paperwork to name a few areas. These are all ensure payment to the agency for the services rendered. And you just thought you were making sure the patients got seen!

Non-operating Revenue

Non-operating revenue is money that comes in that is not tied directly to the services provided. This can include donations, contributions, grants, etc. Agencies can also break this down to the source, separating donations and grants, etc. There are agencies that will depend on non-operating revenue to break even. Many non-profits will function this way. Perhaps they provide a special service to the community or operate at a loss because of being willing to accept all payor sources.

Again, every agency breaks their revenue out differently. It's important to understand what that looks like for your agency if you are being provided the financial statements. Some agencies don't provide their clinical managers with the full report of revenues. It's not unusual. Sometime leadership prefers to not share revenue with staff for various reasons, usually seen with privately owned companies. It's a matter of philosophy, so don't take it personally if this information isn't shared.

Revenue/ Billing Cycle

Other terms you will hear are *Revenue Cycle* or *Billing Cycle*. This is the entire cycle from when a referral is received to the time the claim, or the bill, is sent out the door to be paid. There are people in the agency that are managing this process. Many clinical managers will mistakenly think "oh that's billing, I have nothing to do with that...". The truth is that the billers and revenue cycle managers are the last stop along the process of moving revenue through the agency, and clinical managers have a lot to do with that cycle!

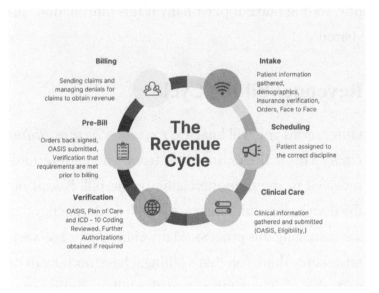

Everything that happens for a patient ends up at the billing door. The taking of information, demographics, insurance coverage, insurance verification and authorization, the completion of the admission visit, documentation completion, scheduling approved disciplines, the timely/accurate OASIS completion, the submission of documentation and the completion of visits in the system.... all fall to the feet of the biller. The computer software will perform its pre-billing checks and either the claim/bill will "drop" and be sent to Medicare or other insurance to be paid or it will be stuck and need human interaction to be fixed. That knock on your door, email in your inbox, or the dreaded bill hold report from the business office needs some help from you as the clinical manager to help solve a puzzle that the revenue cycle team is trying to solve in order for the agency to be paid for services rendered. Pay them mind (no pun intended) as being paid is important in an agency! Often the hold is because of MD orders not being returned, staff documentation not being completed or an authorization that was overlooked. All things that the clinical manager has authority over and can help to resolve by working with their staff or using their relationship with a referring physician.

There are challenges and barriers for a home health agency to be paid for services provided. Under Medicare, as we've established with the regulations, patients have to meet certain criteria in order for the agency to be paid for services rendered. This holds true as well for other insurance coverages. This can be complicated, especially in a highly managed area, or a region that has a lot of managed care and insurance coverage that requires prior authorization. Through the intake process, insurance should be verified, meaning that someone checks to validate that the patient does indeed have the coverage they say they do, and for Medicare, this process includes the verification that another agency does not have the patient already on service. Medicare will pay only one agency for care rendered in home health at a time. Authorizations are also obtained if needed by the insurance company.

The Patient Driven Grouper Model of Payment - PDGM

Much of the revenue in a home health agency is driven by how Medicare pays for care. The Patient Driven Grouper Model (PDGM) has been in effect for a couple of years now and is still considered the new model of payment. As a clinical manager, it is vital that you understand the model and how it works. The provision of care and utilization of visits in an episode is very much on the plate of the clinical manager. High-quality care and clinical outcomes need to be balanced with reimbursement.

The Patient Driven Grouper Model (PDGM) separates payment for a home health episode into two 30-day *periods*. The *episode* for a patient remains at the 60-day mark, with the Plan of Care (POC) or 485 covering the 60-day episode of care.

There are 432 case mix groups for a patient to come under. The groups are determined by the patient's admission source, timing, primary diagnosis and some secondary co-morbidities, and their functional score. It's the completion of the OASIS assessment that drives the overall determination, as well as the admission source. Below is the visual of the PDGM payment model.

Under the Patient-Driven Groupings Model, a 30-day period is grouped into one (and only one) subcategory under each larger colored category. A 30-day period's combination of subcategories places the 30-day period into one of 432 different payment groups.

1. Gastrointestinal tract/Genitourinary system
2. The infectious disease category also includes diagnoses related to neoplasms and blood-forming diseases

*Source: MLN Matters Number: SE19027, 2019

Admission Source

Payment is partially determined from the admission source and timing of the episode. The 1st 30-day period in an admission is usually considered early, the rest of the episodes are late until the patient is re-admitted to home health with at least a 60-day break. The referral source criteria determine if the patient was referred from an institution in the past 14 days or from the community. While captured in the record via the OASIS questions, this information is also validated by CMS claims and corrected in the claims processing. Incorrectly capturing this information can trigger scrutiny.

- Admission source—community or institutional referral

- Timing–early or later episode timing

Clinical Groupings

Clinical Groupings drive the next section of the payment determination or the Home Health Resource Group (HHRG). The clinical group is determined by the primary diagnosis for the patient. This is the diagnosis that is driving the plan of care, the primary reason the patient needs home health services. They lump these into the following categories.

Clinical Groups	The Primary Reason for the Home Health Encounter is to Provide:
Musculoskeletal Rehabilitation	Therapy (physical, occupational or speech) for a musculoskeletal condition
Neuro/Stroke Rehabilitation	Therapy (physical, occupational or speech) for a neurological condition or stroke
Wounds – Post-Op Wound Aftercare and Skin/Non-Surgical Wound Care	Assessment, treatment & evaluation of a surgical wound(s); assessment, treatment & evaluation of non-surgical wounds, ulcers, burns, and other lesions
Behavioral Health Care	Assessment, treatment & evaluation of psychiatric conditions, including substance use disorder
Complex Nursing Interventions	Assessment, treatment & evaluation of complex medical & surgical conditions including IV, TPN, enteral nutrition, ventilator, and ostomies

Clinical Groups	The Primary Reason for the Home Health Encounter is to Provide:
Medication Management, Teaching and Assessment (MMTA)-- • MMTA –Surgical Aftercare • MMTA – Cardiac/Circulatory • MMTA – Endocrine • MMTA – GI/GU • MMTA – ID/Neoplasms/ Blood Diseases • MMTA –Respiratory • MMTA – Other	Assessment, evaluation, teaching, and medication management for a variety of medical and surgical conditions not classified in one of the above listed groups. The subgroups represent common clinical conditions that require home health services for medication management, teaching, and assessment.

*Source: MLN Matters Number: SE19027, 2019

Functional Status

Next is the determination of the functional status. These items are determined through the assessment on the OASIS. Remember that it is the accuracy of the documentation that determines payment. As a clinical manager in home health, it is vital that your staff are doing an accurate *assessment* and not an *interview* with the OASIS items of function. It's not what the patient says they can do–it's what the clinicians assess that the patient can do! The following are the items in the OASIS that drive the functional score.

OASIS Items from which the Functional Score is derived in PDGM
M1800: Grooming
M1810: Current Ability to Dress Upper Body
M1820: Current ability to Dress Lower Body
M1830: Bathing
M1840: Toilet Transferring
M1850: Transferring
M1860: Ambulation/Locomotion
M1032: Risk of Hospitalization

*Source: MLN Matters Number: SE19027, 2019

Co-Morbidities

Co-morbidities also drive payment for the patient. There are a select bunch of diagnosis that paired with the primary diagnosis will create a higher payment. CMS determined through its research that these diagnoses' groupings would have a higher use of resources in home health and, therefore, would qualify for a higher payment. Patients with these diagnosis combinations would likely need to use more nursing, therapy and aide services. It's actually really fascinating stuff to read if you have the time. These details are in the Federal Register when the rules are published.

The Co-morbidities are High, Low and None.

Low = there is a secondary diagnosis that triggers a higher payment

High = there would be two or more diagnoses on the record that interact and trigger a higher payment

None = Speaks for itself

Home Health Resource Group

Of interest is that your software systems have to be built around the payments with the correct groupers to calculate these items which determine your overall payment. There is no one in the back office that manually does this, although it is possible to do. Not a job for me! Below is a grid which shows the HHRG number and letter combinations. For example, a 2CC11–would be a patient admitted from a hospital without another home health episode in the 60 days prior, in the wound category, with high functional needs and no comorbidities.

Position #1	Position #2	Position #3	Position #4	Position #5
Source & Timing	Clinical Group	Functional Level	Co-Morbidity	Placeholder
1 - Community Early	**A** - MMTA Other	**A** - Low	**1** - None	**1**
2 - Institutional Early	**B** - Neuro Rehab	**B** - Medium	**2** - Low	
3 - Community Late	**C** - Wounds	**C** - High	**3** - High	
4 - Institutional Late	**D** - Complex Nursing Interv.			
	E - MS Rehab			
	F — Behavioral Health			
	G — MMTA Surgical Aftercare			
	H — MMTA Cardiac & Circulatory			
	I — MMTA Endrocine			
	J — MMTA GI/GU			
	K — MMTA Infectious Disease			
	L — MMTA Respiratory			

*Source: MLN Matters Number: SE19027, 2019

Low Utilization Payment Adjustments

A Low Utilization Payment Adjustment (LUPA) is where the payment for the care provided is on a per visit basis instead of an episodic basis. This means that instead of being paid by the 30-day period, for example, $2,000, the payment would be $200 for each visit. The payment varies by discipline, nursing, therapy, etc. LUPA thresholds, or limits, range from 2 to 6 visits and are determined by the patient's HHRG. If the threshold for their HHRG is 4, we can provide 4 visits and still be paid for the full episode. If we did 3 visits, it would be a considered a LUPA. We don't like LUPAs because the reimbursement rarely covers the cost of care provided. But we take them in the mix of patients.

LUPA management is something a clinical manager should pay close attention to. In PDGM, we are seeing LUPAs becoming a problem on the 2nd period in a 60-day episode. Yes–we have two chances in home health to have a LUPA in the 60-day episode. Sometimes they can be avoided if we manage patients and know when we are in the LUPA range with our care planning. Every visit has to have a skill to be billable, so don't game the system. It will cause claim denials in the long run. Just be aware of practices on your team. Some things you can control are; making sure the case manager is knowledgeable and sees the patient prior to the 30-day mark to determine if they need to go into the 2nd period. Technology should help us by now to see where we are in the episode and make this process easier for the clinicians in the field, however they need to know why they are looking at this and the impact to the agency. Training and coaching for the clinicians in PDGM will help in managing successfully in the periods.

Expenses

So, we've covered the revenue, the money coming in. Now we need to address the money going out. Because home health is a service industry, the biggest expenses are related to staffing through payroll and benefits. This covers about 70 to 80% of an agency's expenses, give or take. It's like that for most home health agencies. Staff salaries and their insurance, payroll taxes, retirement, etc. all count into that category. And because we are a service industry, we are made or broken by how we staff to provide services. This includes the impact on quality of care and clinical outcomes, and patient satisfaction. Good staffing is important and managing them right is equally important.

Staffing

Let's talk about staffing. I have always contended that staffing is an art and a science and it's something as a clinical manager in home health that you will have to become good at in order to be successful. The art of staffing is the juggling of patient need, staff availability and skill set and keeping everyone happy, reasonably so anyway. On one hand, you have the pressures of meeting the needs of new referrals and on the other, the patients already on service. There are a lot of admission, discharge and transfer activities occurring all day long. In addition, you have staffing turnover, call outs, vacations, trainings and meetings to contend with. It's an art and science, to be sure, balancing all of those needs.

When we look at staffing in home health, we have to approach it in a couple of ways. Each agency will have their own nuances, along with the preferences of the financial staff who are doing the budgeting. It will pay off for you to work directly with the financial team at your agency to better understand how they are budgeting and determining the staffing needs. I have found the best approaches are those that focus on the two factors of patient census and visits. The total number of patients a RN case manager is expected to manage divided into the census will roughly give you how many full time RN case managers you will need to have on staff. The other number to consider is historical visits. Using your productivity expectations, you can forecast the staffing need for your agency or your team.

There are a few things to note with determining staffing needs. One FTE (full-time equivalent) does not work every day. There are vacations, sick time, holidays and in-service days you need to consider when staffing. These are days that the staff are not making visits but are still an FTE. On average, look at how many days a year one FTE is available to do visits. Do this by considering the average RN; how many vacation days do they take, sick days, holidays and training/in-service days do you require? This can be eye opening for some folks and can shed light on staffing overages. Bringing together all of these factors can provide a good idea of where you are with staffing balanced with demands at your agency.

Productivity

Then there is productivity... I can tell you I have traveled the country talking to hundreds of clinical managers, and not one ever told me how much they enjoy talking about productivity! Over time, we have placed great emphasis on the efficiencies of how staff are doing their work and need to measure this to ensure we are tracking with the budget and to stay within our financial means. Think of this: with 70 to 80% of the expense budget being related to staffing, any over-staffing can have a detrimental impact on the agency. So, making sure we are efficient and stay that way is huge.

Over time, we have made mistakes with the emphasis on productivity from a clinical operations standpoint. The measure has been fraught with much emotion and dismay from the clinicians and clinical managers. It's almost as though we have seen the measure of productivity to equate to how good a clinician we are, how much we care and take care of our patients. Please realize that it's just a measure, and nothing more. It has nothing to do with the value of yourself as a human being! I jest, but there is a lot of feeling around this measure. I have seen agencies that have allocated another FTE to do all the crazy calculations on weighting visits with productivity measurement. Don't go there. Doing this is not a value add to the agency by any means. Weighting driving, meetings by type, coming to the office, dropping off lab specimens, etc., which are all really accounted for already.

I have been to many agencies, and everyone does this differently, but the best advice I can give you is to measure a visit as a visit, and not "weight" the measure with extraneous things. It should go without saying that admission and resumption of care visits take longer, as do some particular patient care needs. There will be variability in how staff perform to your organization's method of measuring productivity. This should reflect in their caseloads, and you, as the clinical manager, should be able to know the causes of the variances. The overall goal should be to have a productivity overall that meets the standard set by your organization.

As the clinical manager, you must balance the art and science. You would know that nurse Sally has a caseload of complex patients with IVs, wound vacs and various lengthy treatments, and would expect her productivity to be lower. But that is balanced with nurse Jane, who doesn't do admissions, and has a larger caseload but can easily see 6 patients a day and complete her documentation. Balance is the key.

There is value, however, in periodically analyzing the days of your staff. There can be a lot of time wasted on a clinician's day. Looking at how they are spending their time and how long they take to accomplish a task is helpful and can provide you with insight into areas to streamline. Often documentation becomes unwieldy due to well-meaning projects that added documentation but removed none. Look at how many times a week you require the staff to come into the office, and how many things they are required to do that do not require the license of a clinician to do. Very insightful information to be found in taking on that exercise.

Turnover

Managing staffing costs are prime for a clinical manager, included in this is the cost of turnover. We'll talk more about managing people in that section, but it's important to know that the churn of staff increases staffing expenses. There is the expense of overtime or additional pay and work for staff that are trying to cover the staffing vacancies. If staff are salaried, it can be in the additional stressors added to them because of vacancies, or even as the clinical manager going out to make visits. Your job is not done when you aren't there. Hiring travelers to fill in the vacancies can be very expensive.

Turnover has a cost both in the churn of clinicians and in the hidden costs of 'covering' the vacancy. According to SHRM turnover costs 6 to 9 months of the workers' annual salary to replace them in recruiting and training costs. (The HRmeister, 2017). For a $80k annual nurse salary, that can be from $40k to $60k per nurse. That's significant when you add it all up together.

Supplies

Another expense area is in supplies, and we are not talking the pen and paper, but the medical supplies for an agency. This is another area that the clinical manager needs to have a handle on. How are we using supplies, ordering, and ensuring we are not wasting them? Trunks can eat supplies, as well as not billing for them when able to for a patient. Having a handle on this is huge. Many agencies have resorted to drop shipping of supplies, and no longer having large stock on hand in the office. This reduces loss not only from stock in trunks, but from the costs of staff taking the time to travel back and forth to the office to get supplies. The time it takes for a nurse or therapist to pick up and deliver supplies can be hours and can impact overall productivity and efficiency. Their skills would be put to better use providing clinical care rather than running errands. It would also lead to a less frustrated and frazzled clinical team.

Budgeting

If you are like me, I like to run and hide when it comes time to budget. The view of my CFO standing at my door with her calculator in hand still gives me chills. Over the years, I have trained myself to like the process and the painstaking runs of calculating revenues and expenses to get to a final workable document. It's helpful to consider the budget as a plan and a forecast. Looking ahead to project out the plan for the next year and testing out whether raises are affordable, or we can plan new laptops are some things the budgeting process can bring. I have found is that it provides the clinical manager with the opportunity to review current year performance and plan for the next year. Targeting areas that need improvement and setting goals to achieve them. It's such a highly educational opportunity for a clinical manager to take part in, You learn to understand the calculations and assumptions from the financial team, and potentially uncover cost saving opportunities for the organization.

We use budgets throughout the year to compare the current financial performance to the budgeted amounts. Financial statements will report comparisons, either better or worse, to budget. This is a very necessary process, as it compares the 'plan' to the 'actual'. It displays what you thought you could do, compared to what you actually did. Variances are important to understand. A variance could be positive, where the agency performed better than expected, or it could be negative, where the agency performed worse than expected.

It is often the role of the clinical manager to understand why those variances occurred, particularly when they are negative. Identifying what happened and then putting in a plan to correct it or ensure that it didn't happen again are what the clinical manager should do. Understanding the interaction between your actions and decisions as a clinical manager to the financial performance is a skill you need to have and to build on. For example, deciding to allow a newly hired nurse to spend more office time with their preceptor reduced the productivity produced by both nurses and increased the staffing costs for the month, as you called in a per diem/casual nurse, to cover patient visits. An increase in census did not cover this staffing overage, however, you made the choice after conferring with your Director, to allow better training for a great hire and reducing the workload stress for the preceptor.

Managing expenses is the responsibility of the clinical manager for their team. With 70 to 80% of the expenses coming directly from staffing, this is where you will need to understand the balance of your actions and decisions to the financial performance. Digging into those variances is on your list of responsibilities. It's helpful to understand the positive variances as well. It's nice to see a kick up in revenue coming in, more than expected. But what caused it? Was it a higher volume of admissions? Was it better OASIS accuracy–may be an impact of recent training?

Benchmarks

Most agencies will use benchmarks, or Key Performance Indicators (KPIs). These are measures which compare your results to others. These measures can be national or regional–comparing to agencies across a geographic region. They can also be historical for the agency, comparing past performance to current.

Benchmarks are really great to use, as they compare your performance and identify areas that need work.

Attention needs to be paid however to the benchmark itself, as to the reliability of the source, and how it's measured. For example; is it a best practice measure—like the top 10%? Or is it the average? Is it regional or national? Not understanding the measure should not be used to discredit the measure. "That's the measure for large national agencies that can achieve that, not for our small agency. We're different..." While there are differences in some areas, usually it's not the case. Don't get into the habit of dismissing any benchmarks, thinking they do not apply to your circumstances. It's a trap for excuses. Don't go there. If you find you are not measuring up to a benchmark or a KPI, dig into it. Ask why and find the reasons. Digging in to understand the variances will get you further in your career than passing it off as a "bad measure". Why is the national cost per visit of a nurse at $150 and your agency is at $250? Are your staff paid more or are you in the salary range of your area? Is your productivity measuring up or have you weighted so much and given points to so many activities that you don't know what your average visits per day are? Are your driving times really higher than other agencies?

Don't be afraid to compare your measures. It can provide great insight and guidance to help control costs. With margins so small in many agencies – (the difference between expense and revenue = the bottom-line) it's very important you have the incentive to look for ways to improve performance and be more cost effective.

Best Practices

As you work at understanding the finances, you will also expose your financial management abilities or lack thereof. Being successful means not only building on what you know but identifying what you don't and creating a plan to address those areas. Its valuable to know where you stand.

I have been pretty forthcoming about where my weakness was when I first became a manager. I knew nothing about finances, nothing. Understand where you need to grow, make your list. No one but you need to see it. Seek ways to improve. Take the steps to ask questions of your finance team. Meet 1/1 with them if they are willing. Look for training or courses and read books on finance. You may need to step out of the home healthcare arena a bit and into a hospital or health system lingo. Dig into the details and don't be afraid of the numbers. Ask questions when you don't understand something. Identifying your needs, focusing on growing your knowledge, will help you succeed.

Chapter Five

Pillar # 3: Clinical Knowledge

CLINICAL

As a clinical manager, most agencies expect that you have come into the role with some level of clinical knowledge in the home health or hospice arena. As a licensed clinician as the federal rules require, you must at least have had enough experience and training to pass the licensure requirements. The federal regulations require:

"§484.115 (c) provides that a clinical manager must be a licensed physician, physical therapist, speech-language pathologist, occupational therapist, audiologist, social worker, or a registered nurse."

As mentioned in the Regulations chapter of this book, states may have more stringent requirements for the role of a clinical manager with further education and experience requirements. Most organizations will require a certain level of experience either from a clinical standpoint or managerial standpoint. Ideally, the minimal requirement should be a substantiative 3-to-5-year experience as a clinician in home health or hospice and at least one year of supervisory experience. Having an acute care background and home health or hospice experience would be ideal, giving a well-rounded clinical experience.

However, in these times in 2022, these key positions are hard to fill. I can honestly say that I have not seen the level of recruitment and advertising out there for clinical managers across the country until recently. It is likely agencies will make concessions to get positions filled, and ambitious folks with little experience will take the role of clinical manager. If that is you, or someone you know, I'm glad you've picked up this book!

It's that sink or swim approach to filling open clinical manager positions that prompted the creation of this book and The Clinical Manager Source (http://theclin icalmanagersource.com)

Clinical Procedure Manuals

Okay, back to Clinical Knowledge! As a clinical manager, you will be the source that your staff call when they have a clinical question regarding patient care for a particular treatment order or procedure. You should never assume that you need to know absolutely everything about clinical care to be a clinical manager. It is your role to ensure your staff are competent and provide good clinical care in line with accepted clinical practice. You do not need to be the only source. Good, safe care is the priority. At times, you will learn right along with the clinicians, particularly when there is a new piece of equipment or a novel approach to care in the home.

However, you need to make certain that your staff has the resources, training, and competencies they need to perform a procedure or to use a piece of equipment. You also need to ensure that they are following the agency guidelines for care. It is best practice to have procedure manuals available for the clinical team. These should have been vetted and reviewed through the quality processes at your agency and formally accepted as the standards of practice. Typically, the quality leader and a team of clinicians complete this review to ensure the procedures meet recognized clinical standards and can be safely performed in the home by agency staff. Accreditation bodies and states have different requirements for this process, but all align in that staff need an up-to-date reference to ensure they are performing patient care in line with clinical standards of care. A dusty binder on the bottom shelf of your office with the clinical procedures does not help to meet the standard of having accessible information available to field clinicians. How do they have ready access to this information? Ideally, it should be available on-line or in an intranet type of internal virtual availability. This would make the information readily accessible 24/7 and permit nearly instant updates when needed.

These clinical procedures need to reflect the home setting. Not all clinical procedure manuals out there do this. There are nuances to the care in the home that are only reflected in clinical procedure manuals focused on these areas. These procedure manuals can protect your staff, or they can cause liability issues if harm comes to a patient from care rendered outside of the accepted procedures. The agency or the individual clinician can be sued or have their license placed in jeopardy if they injure a patient from the care provided. Following the accepted procedures protects them, and not following the rules can risk liability if harm arises from the care. Therefore, the procedures need to reflect standard clinical practice in the home and be vetted and accepted by the agency leadership.

Having access and coordinating resources for your clinical team to become adept and competent in the clinical care that your agency provides is part of your role as a clinical manager. Care in the home has become more and more complex over time. We see more equipment used and medications delivered in the home that used to be provided only in the inpatient setting. As technology and innovation enables more people to live longer lives, we'll continue to see this grow. I can recall my surprise, a very long time ago, when I first came to home care from the hospital setting and visited the home of a man with ALS on a ventilator that he and his wife managed on their own. Over 30 years ago, my experience was that kind of care was only done in the ICU, not in the home, managed by a family member! Consider the modernization of the home medical equipment. There are smaller, more portable machines and technologies that were not seen a few years ago. There are infusions of medications we can manage safely and other treatments not previously considered. This enhances the quality of life we can deliver in the home setting. It's really mindboggling to consider.

Patient Population Data Sources

In order to be well prepared and ensure you have the right resources at your fingertips, you need to understand who your agency serves. Identifying what type of clinical needs they have, and determine how you can work to ensure your staff are prepared to provide top-notch care. Knowing the most common conditions, diagnosis, home treatments (wounds, ortho, post stroke etc.) can help you to plan specific education or competencies to better serve your patient population. Before jumping in on your own to dig up data about your service area, check within your organization to see if some data mining has already been done. This could be in the sales and marketing department, where they would have studied referral sources. This could also be in the finance department, where they may have reviewed insurance companies in the area. Also check with the quality/performance improvement folks as they may have access to the OASIS data that can provide further view of reports of clinical groupings providing insight into patient diagnoses.

Reviewing data or gathering data from your sources is a first step. Do not re-create the wheel. However, be sure that you know what you want to ask of the data. Looking at the top clinical diagnoses, top referral sources and other indicators picked up in the OASIS or in your documentation system can make this data review easier and cleaner. It's very easy to get buried in reviewing data reports and records. Stay true to your questions about the data as you go through this review. I love to look at data and review aspects of a service area or nuances related to referral sources. That being said, it's so easy to get lost in the information as there is so much of it! Stick to what you want to know about your patient population so you aren't tempted to run down a rabbit hole. Validate what your findings are. They should align with what you are seeing in the census. Looking at who your agency serves will help to define the focus of clinical education and competency that you and your team need in order to have successful clinical outcomes and please patients and referral sources. Looking at your agency data can guide you to focus on the specific education needs of your team.

Does the agency receive a lot of referrals for patients with wound care, or IV therapy or aftercare for some special type of surgery? if you have a lot of wound care, ensuring competencies in wound management by coordinating training with care approaches and different products with your staff would be a good idea. Do you need to have a clinician on staff or a contract with special wound care training, such as a Wound Ostomy Continence Nurse (WOCN)? Do staff know who to call or have a consult with when they have questions about wound care and healing?

We could take the same approach with IVs and specific infusion pumps or drugs. Coordinating training and resources for staff will carry a long way. Not only would you be working to ensure that the staff are competent, and the clinical care is top-notch, but you also ensure that the staff feel supported, and the agency is safe-guarding their success as employees. Feeling prepared and well educated can go a long way in staff satisfaction.

Patient populations with specific needs require specific care and training from the clinical team. Aligning training, education and competencies of your clinical team to what they are seeing on a day-to-day basis will go far. I will also stress that you cannot address the specific care needs of your entire patient population. There will be cases that are referred which require something you hadn't thought of, or expected with your review of the patient data. Or you may find you had a few complex care needs patients that were referred, but have had none of the same for months. Make sure you're not focusing all the training needs on one-off cases that may have needed specialized care, but you'll likely not have again.

Consider ensuring training and education for cases that are high volume, high risk and problem prone. This is a time-tested quality improvement method. In home health, we see a lot of chronic patients with diabetes, cardiac issues, and pulmonary diseases. Are our staff trained and confident in care for these patient populations? Do we have adequate resources for patient education and clinical team education and competency?

What are the areas in your population that are high risk? This is interesting to consider. I have always considered what the staff are doing *to* patients and what could go wrong if they aren't trained adequately? When determining what is "high risk" IVs, wounds, catheters—all fall into this category. A home care nurse may not see them every day, and a lot can go wrong if staff are not competent in these areas. Infection, emergency room use, hospitalization and death are all risks. The agency gets measured on the outcomes of re-hospitalization and ER use and these statistics compared to other agencies. How do you perform in these measures for patients in these categories? It can be eye opening to review.

The problem prone areas require a further review. What causes issues for patients at your agency? Is it timing? Is it a particular care need? Is it a multidisciplinary team patient need? Could it be weekend referrals, or later Friday afternoon hospital discharges? Are these patients having issues and getting re-hospitalized or using the ER more than others?

Asking these questions during your data review is helpful in determining what kind of orientation, training, and ongoing education your team needs. This may point out areas in which a process needs to change.

Orientation, Training and Competencies

While it's not always up to the clinical manager to determine what the full orientation of new staff comprises, it is a very important process for the clinical manager to be engaged in. I will say this a few times in this book, and I hope I drive it home. *Your success or failure as a clinical manager will be determined by the work your team does.* They are now the most important people driving your success. Without their excellent performance, the measure your management capabilities are assessed by will be substandard. Working to assure their success will be your success.

Now that you have completed the review of the type of patient you are caring for, the risks and issues of the care included. It's time to ensure that your staff are prepared and knowledgeable about the care the patients' need.

Orientation is a crucial part of the successful clinician's career in home health or hospice. Too often we will have a great need for staff and will have clinicians on their own before they are really ready. They may not have really understood some aspects of the training and with so much at stake, it is vital that the clinical manager ensure the staff are competent. While the orientation forms and checklists help to guide what a new staff member needs, it is the follow up and oversight from a clinical manager that ensures the retention and comprehension of the training.

Taking some additional time with new staff members, making ride-along home visits and performing case reviews help to ensure that they are 'getting' home health or hospice. You are their teacher and guide and supporting them to learn what they need to will go far in their satisfaction and retention and help in achieving the clinical and financial goals of the team overall.

As mentioned earlier, you do not need to be the expert at everything clinical, but you need to guide your staff to the right resources for what they need. Trouble with wound care? Connect to a WOCN or product vendor for training. Lots of IVs? Ensure competency and comfort with pumps and site management.

In larger agencies, the clinical manager is not always the one deciding what their staff will have for education and orientation. Often, this is part of the quality or education departments. However, it *IS* the role of the clinical manager to suggest, connect, and request more resources and training for staff as seen fit. Everyone is working for the same goals as you are with your team. Since you are on the front lines, you can see the needs more clearly and your input is very valuable.

Best Practices

There are a lot of resources out there for a clinical manager to reference to ensure your own knowledge in clinical care. Access them and refer to them often. There are procedure manuals, research and articles on home care and hospice nursing aspects you need to be aware of to be successful in your role. Gather these resources together and share them with your team as you are able. This could be obtaining a subscription to a nursing magazine or a journal to share with your team. Discuss the information at a team meeting and bring resources in from outside sources, like a local hospital or a vendor product, to discuss care methods being seen or implemented in the inpatient setting that may affect patient care in the home.

Cultivate excellence in your clinical team, engage them in improving their practice and encourage them to share what they may have learned by reading an article or attending a conference. There is information out there. Bring it in to your team. You'll find that by doing so, you will cultivate a culture of clinical excellence. Building on this with employees will add value to the work life. Working for you is not just about getting the visits and the documentation done, it will be about being the best clinicians. Knowing they can rely on you as their manager to help access information they need to provide better care will build trust and improve retention.

Chapter Six

PILLAR #4: PEOPLE

PEOPLE

M anaging people effectively is another of the pillars of knowledge that a clinical manager needs to possess. This is likely to be one of the hardest, easiest, most challenging and stimulating of all the pillars. There will be days it seems everyone is troublesome on your team, and days that you wonder if you're suited for management because of the struggles with staff. Really, the job would be so easy if there were no staff and no patients! Then there are the days when everything is clicking, and things are working as they should.

Being in a service industry, our product is our people and our customers are people with families and friends. As a clinical manager, you will need to balance these two populations that can sometimes have contrasting needs.

We are in the business of healthcare to care for our patients and their families. In the role of clinical manager, it's important to understand that our patients should be our priority. The patient comes first motto. However, in recent years, it has become apparent, with changing employee needs, changing motivations, and retention concerns, that we need to put employees first. The satisfaction, engagement and commitment of our employees matters greatly in how successfully we care for our patients.

I have always practiced with the focus that the patient come first. But in my role as manager, I learned quickly that my commitment was not only to the patient, but to the people I was putting in front of the patients we were serving. As a manager, you are only as good as the staff on your team. Your success is directly reflected in their performance. The visual I always used when describing this concept to new managers was to turn the organizational chart upside down.

A typical organizational chart shows the leader is in charge, with everyone reporting upward to the CEO. It looks like the leader is the most important person, sitting at the top of the organization, at the top of the heap. While this role certainly carries much responsibility, the reality is that it's not the most important role in an organization. The same goes for your role. While you gained responsibility by becoming a manager, you didn't become more vital. There was not a coronation when you became a manager. The most important people in the organization are those that care directly for the patient. They are vital to the organization. This is an essential concept to remember.

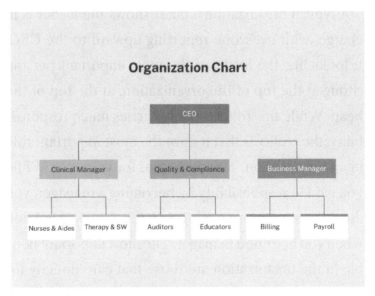

By turning the organizational chart upside down, it puts the focus on who is most important in an organization. We serve patients. They should be here as well, as they are the focus of everything. But in truth, as a manager, it's the people that serve the patients that are the most important. How they perform directly affects the care of the patient and the overall performance of the agency. It's their actions and inactions that drive everything.

With the patient at the center of everything we do, the people who we place to care for the patient need our support and help to ensure they can provide the best care possible to patients. It's the role of the clinical manager to provide that support and guidance, ensuring staff are prepared as clinicians and supported as employees.

There is a lot to know when dealing with employees. Sometimes how we choose to interact can be ripe with minefields. This is an area where you will need to ensure that you follow the organization's personnel policies and to seek help from human resources whenever you are unsure of your skill in dealing with an employee situation. As a clinical manager, you will be engaged in the selection of staff, interviewing, possibly checking references, hiring, coaching, disciplining and terminating employees. Focusing time and attention on building skills in these areas will help your career. I will stress that *no one* is truly successful in a management or leadership role that can't manage and interact with employees.

Selecting the Right, Qualified People

One of the most important tasks you will have is selecting new hires for your team. Hiring to the needs of your team and your patient population are important considerations. Are you looking for a special skill such as wound care or IV skills? Maybe experience on using your software or substantial experience in home health or hospice? Considering balancing skill sets is a valid concern. Having too much of one and not enough of another can be problematic. If you have a majority of new to home care nurses with 2 years and less experience already on the team, you might hire for more experience. The same would be to balance out the LPN with the RN, ensuring you have adequate RN staff, or PT to PTA, OT to COTA.

What about their "fit"? Even though home care and hospice can be a solitary practice, they are part of the overall team. Do their career goals, education and commitment to the profession align with the rest of your team? Is this a person you can see yourself working with? Having others from the team take part in the interview process can help you decide on the individual.

Occasionally, you may also be tempted to hire someone who is not quite qualified for the role but has potential. I don't want to deter you from growing people into roles, but do this cautiously and with a plan to train and educate the individual. On clinical teams, this could mean hiring a LPN or an aide who is about to graduate from RN school. While this can work, it takes planning and commitment to ensure they gain the experience they really need to be clinically strong. There is a lot of time that needs to be dedicated to having this be successful. However, I have seen it work really well, and I have seen it fail miserably. The candidate needs to be invested in the process and the agency. If you don't have the time or the resources to commit to growing the candidate, it may not be the best action to fill an open position.

Reference Checks

This is one of the more challenging aspects of people management, especially because of the constraints that go along with the process. Reference checks can sometimes be just a validation that the individual worked there for a certain period. No other information is usually shared, especially if it's bad. The liability of tarnishing someone's career through this process is very real and has led to past or current employers withholding any details of performance. If you are able to connect personally, I've always found it helpful to know if they would hire the candidate back. There can be a lot gleaned from this conversation. Additionally, it can be useful to have informal insight to past work experiences with co-workers. I've worked with managers who won't hire anyone unless they've been referred by someone already on staff.

Interviewing

Of course, you also ensure that you are following standard operating procedures for interviewing, ensuring the rights of the candidates. It is illegal to ask candidates about their religion, age, birthplace/country of origin, disability, gender, marital status, sexual orientation, children, pregnancy, race, color, or ethnicity. It is vital that you understand these areas to avoid in order to ensure the appropriateness of your interview questions and protect the candidate's rights.

My preference was always to do the initial interview of a candidate myself, and if they checked all of my boxes, I would invite them back to have a second interview with the team and again with me right after the team interview. This process did a few things. I could assess the candidate before the team, ensuring that they were qualified, and I felt they would be a match for the team. The second interview with the team gave them the chance to assess the candidate and be engaged in the process of hiring team members. I appreciated several other invested people also looked over the prospective new team member. I liked to meet with them right after they met with the team, not only to 'see' them again, but to assess their response to the team interview. Did they like the group and see themselves working with them? And it also gave me the chance to see how they would respond under pressure. It's difficult to be interviewed by a group of your peers.

Job interviewing and hiring are not something I enjoy doing. I would rather review financial statements and try to explain a bad variance than go through the hiring process. I had to work hard at interviewing and hiring 'right'. To this day, I shy away from the interview to hire. Great interviewees that perform well in the interview have bowled me over and then bomb out 2 weeks into the job. I have hired people with great resumes, good answers to my questions that have not shown up after a few days on the job. I have also hired some really great people that to this day are still people I like and admire and are active in the healthcare arena. This is an imperfect process, for sure, but one you must undertake to have any staff!

The challenge is that you are hiring people with lives, personal challenges and experiences that we could only imagine. They have desires and goals for their lives and careers, and you are a piece of that story. As much as we are assessing them, they are assessing us. Trying to see if the job we are describing and offering is something they want to take on and if it will fit in with their lives. That is why being honest and being real yourself in an interview is best. Pitching the job as the greatest thing since sliced bread, with the benefits of flexibility and great hours, may not entirely be true. It's disheartening to hear from new staff that they feel they misrepresented the role when the work isn't done by 3 PM and they aren't drinking pina coladas at home by their pool and they don't realize the paperwork burdens. Some people will hear what they want to hear, to justify the job change. It's best to be transparent and truthful about the job to new candidates.

My first interview to move to home health from the local hospital involved the supervisor telling me the kinds of homes I would go into. I heard stories of bedbugs, roaches and rotten floors. She really laid it out to me, and honestly I know I wasn't hearing anything except the hours being all day shift with one weekend every 6 weeks and Christmas only on-call, if at all. The hours and hours of paperwork, the endless driving and the on-call rotations didn't scare me. But then I found out what she meant!

A few words of wisdom in hiring. Develop your own method of interviewing candidates. There is no one right way, but the best thing is to listen to the candidate, ensure they are the one doing the most talking. It's your time to hear from them why they want to work for you and how they will fit on the team. While you want to describe the role and the realities, don't spend all of your time talking. Asking why they want to leave their current job, or why they left if not employed, will offer insight into what they want out of a role as well as potentially uncovering any obvious red flags for you.

Approach the interview as a conversation. Don't pepper the candidate with questions. Start out with small talk and then move into exploring the candidate's experience and reasons for looking for a change. Honestly, I always use the weather to break the ice or something funny or significant that may have occurred in the community. Stay very far away from politics in any of your conversations and keep away from it at work at all.

Deciding on a Candidate

It is also a terrible idea to hire a candidate that you are unsure about just because you are desperate to fill a position. This usually ends badly and makes matters worse. With poor performance to manage, the fallout from a desperation hire can include the inability to manage a caseload, poor documentation, patient satisfaction and care outcomes, and frustration from the rest of the team who may try to fill in the gaps caused by a bad hire. There is truly nothing worse for the morale of a team than the manager tolerating poor performance either through hiring someone new that can't perform or by keeping someone with poor performance to fill a staffing need. Avoid the warm body hire, no matter how frantic you are for staff.

The other advice I have for you is to listen to your gut with hiring. If something about a candidate is causing you to pause, pay attention. The mistakes I have made in hiring my career have largely been when I didn't listen to that inner voice. As a clinician, you likely possess some level of intuition. Explore what that voice is telling you and whether it's something that can be overcome or not. A candidate can look great on paper and interview like a star, but if something is causing you to pause... listen to it. It doesn't mean it is that they wouldn't be an outstanding employee, it could be something else.

I once was desperately looking to replace a vacancy in our financial leadership at my agency. I had two candidates to choose from. One very qualified on paper, interviewed well, would have made a nice fit on the team. The other was qualified as well, but had no healthcare experience. Something made me pause on the 1st candidate. There was something off and I couldn't figure it out. I hired the second candidate, and it turned out well. The first candidate was about to be fired from his role for some 'improper accounting' I later learned. In retrospect, it was likely the energy the candidate was putting out. He really marketed himself for the job, and maybe there was an air of desperation I picked up on. Listen to that voice!

Coaching

It is the job of the clinical manager to coach your staff to be successful. This is a daily job, teaching, reviewing and coaching your team to comply with the regulations and manage their caseload of patients. Reviewing their plans of care, documentation and discussing their plans for their patients helps them to succeed as clinicians. You will assist them in managing patient expectations, clinical outcomes, and overall satisfaction. You'll manage the schedule and ensure proper utilization of resources for the census.

There will be times when the daily coaching goes beyond the usual day-to-day operations. This could involve assisting team members to achieve specific career goals, such as additional training or certifications. Often agencies have their staff identify some specific goals for their own development during the performance review process. Coaching and guiding staff to achieve these goals should be part of your role. This could involve gaining funding for a team member to attend a wound care conference and to bring back the education to benefit the clinical team. Or assisting a staff member to be certified in OASIS review, or IV therapy or any number of specialty areas to codify their expertise.

Coaching is the fun stuff, assisting your team to grow and to be better clinicians. It provides them with support and assists to retain clinicians. It helps them to gain confidence and moves the team forward professionally. However, there will also come times when you will need to counsel a staff member because of poor performance or error. While this is not a fun task for a manager to do, it is very necessary to ensure that you are guiding your team to be successful and that includes addressing poor performance.

Counseling

I realize I have said this often in this chapter, however, it's really an important point to drive home. Putting up with bad behavior and poor performance affects the entire team. It's not just you not having to deal with it or the staff member getting away with it, it's a kick in the teeth to the other hardworking, good performing people on the team who show up every day and put their best effort in. While you may think they don't notice, they do. It affects them, and their incentive to continue to try. Why should they pick up the slack for poor performance on the team? There will always be the give and take among the staff. When someone is struggling with a difficult caseload, the team will pitch in and do more. But asking them to do it routinely because one nurse can't do their job, just deflates their confidence in the team, in the agency and in you as their manager. This type of environment can lead to turnover of outstanding employees,

Poor performance and unacceptable behavior need to be addressed, or chaos will ensue. While you need to be tolerant of people when then may have a bad day on a rare occasion, you will need to find a balance and make sure you are dealing with continued bad behavior and performance. So, what does this mean? Should you issue written warnings to all staff that dare to cross any line you may draw? While you need to follow the guidelines, your agency lays out for this process of formal discipline, you also need to ensure that you have a process to follow before that written warning. Most organizations will have a prescribed process to follow because of the legal nature of the proceedings. Be aware of it and follow-it closely.

A formal disciplinary step should never be a surprise to an employee. They should well know their continued action or inaction will begin the progressive disciplinary process. But well before that, you should have talked with them about your concerns. I refer to these conversations as a "hey what's going on with you?

Lately this has been happening..." This should NEVER be done in a public place. Disciplining or correcting an employee needs to be done in private. Otherwise, it's demeaning and can make the situation worse, not to mention how others would respond to you treating someone like that.

Have a conversation in person preferably, face to face. This always helps and creates an environment of seriousness. Keeping the conversation private helps the employee to realize they have crossed a line. And having a private conversation with you helps to define what the issue is and how it can be fixed. Often, there is something that can be done to move the employee back into performing well. In these conversations, it is best to approach it as a concerned person who wants to help. Let them know what you have observed, and why it's an issue. Let them tell their side. Listen, but within reason keeping the attention to time to avoid becoming a psychologist. Discuss what needs to happen and by when, so you are clear about what they need to do. Offer help if you can.

In my experience, these situations often can be resolved. Maybe a piece of equipment is not working correctly–such as a laptop. Or there is some personal stressor. Offering a fix to the equipment and/or a day off to deal with a family issue can ease the burden for the employee. It can show you care, and will help them be successful.

Depending on your organization's policies, make sure you have some level of documentation of this discussion and the agreement with the employee about what needs to happen. It has been my practice to have informal documentation in my desk or in my computer under lock and key to these kinds of general counseling with employees. Most of the time I end up destroying them after a period, because the performance or behavior was corrected. However, in progressive disciplinary processes, its handy to have documentation of what occurred prior and the discussions, steps and actions taken to support and guide the employee.

This information can support the steps you take for written disciplinary action up to and including termination. There is nothing worse than going to terminate an employee and having nothing to stand on in their file to support the action. It can definitely be an eye opener and clear evidence of putting up with poor performance without taking action to correct it. This reflects right back to the clinical manager.

Responding to and supporting your team through performance issues helps to establish clear boundaries. The team knows where the lines are and that you will respond to poor performance. They also learn that you are there to support them when stuff happens, because it does and it will happen to all of us. Being fair and consistent in this process as the manager will gain you miles of respect from the team, from upper management and human resources.

Exiting Employees

There will come a time when you must fire an employee. Maybe you've done all you can for an employee's performance improvement, and they are not responding, and there is nothing left to do but separate them from the agency. This is never easy, and it shouldn't be. Taking away someone's livelihood and ability to provide for their family is a serious action. It is also full of potholes where you can make mistakes, which will have legal ramifications for you and the agency. My advice is to ALWAYS involve the human resources in the termination process, ensuring there is another review of the documentation and processes you have followed to get to the point of termination. Make sure you are following the organization's policy. Some will require a human resource representative to do the firing or be in the room with you when you do.

Keeping underperformers or putting up with terrible behavior brings down the rest of the team. It's unfortunate to have to terminate an employee, but it will be something you will have to do as a clinical manager at some time in your career.

Communication

Communication is important in any work setting but is a challenge in the home health and hospice arenas simply because the work is out in the community. There are days that go by without seeing a staff member face to face. Often, you will only lay eyes on them when they come in for team meetings or caseload reviews with you. This makes communication with employees really important and ensuring they all receive the same messages and information is vital.

Nothing can be more frustrating than developing a communication method that people do not use. This can be as easy as email or an announcement in the clinical software when a user logs in. What I have found, looking at this as part of operational reviews as a consultant, is that communication has to be balanced. While you may want to communicate and share a lot of information with your staff, you can over communicate. If staff have too many emails or voice mails to wade through, they won't listen or read them. They are really busy and getting to their patients is their priority.

I have seen agencies that will have, and I am not kidding, hundreds of emails and voice mails to get through before they see patients. Literally, I have seen clinicians spending an hour or two before heading out to see patients. If your staff are spending over 5 to 10 minutes every morning catching up on communi-cation–emails/voice mails etc.–it's too much! These agencies were communicating, for certain, but not every staff person needed to hear all of it.

The key to effective communication is to decide how you will communicate and who needs to know what. Decide how you will routinely communicate with the team for routine things, such as general announce-ments. This could be in a weekly or bi-weekly email or voicemail. Something that an employee can read that week and to be up to date. Think of this as introducing a new employee, or a revised policy or a reminder about a meeting next week, etc.

Other communication needs to center on patient care. The clinical software should be where this takes place, if the functionality is in the system. Sending this communication outside of the software, such as in email, creates another separate place for clinical documentation. It needs to stay in the patient's record, not in the email system. These situations could include a patient needing a visit today, needs to be sent to the case manager and the scheduler, and not necessarily to the entire clinical team. Make a plan for this communication, focusing on effectiveness, need to know, and follow-up. While sometimes you have to go outside of the system, try your best not to.

Urgent communication is another area. Information that the staff needs to know as soon as possible is likely because of an urgent situation. How you communicate urgent information should be a method that grabs the staff's attention, and they must respond to it. Maybe a mass text to the team (not patient information), or a flag in the clinical documentation software that they must read before proceeding to a patient record. The trick here is to not combine methods. If a staff received a communication from you using this urgent method, they would pay immediate attention. It should not be a method that is used for routine communication, otherwise the message will blend into the rest, and not be given the attention it needs from the staff.

Communication is a two-way street, and there needs to be an expectation of accountability to read the communication you send . This means that they will commit to reading their email, voicemail and texts and respond appropriately. It's cringeworthy to hear a staff member say, "oh I never read those emails!". However, you set up the communication methods for your team, set the expectations for the staff, and make sure they know what you are expecting. Hold them accountable to it as well. It is a performance issue if staff cannot receive the communication you send. Of course, it needs to be a reasonable amount, so ensure the expectation is workable within their day and productivity expectations.

As a manager, you will also need to communicate upward to your boss and their boss periodically. This is something that you need to learn to not shy away from and to make certain you are communicating what they need to know. Nothing is worse for your performance as a manager for bad news regarding your team to come from someone other than yourself. Reporting when things go awry is a good practice. It shows that you are taking ownership of a problem. Of course also reporting what you have done to mitigate the situation is also good practice. Don't leave all the problem solving up to your boss, it's your job to own things.

Communicate regularly with your superiors, be visible to them. Often, there will be an established cadence of reporting with your superior. However, if not, seek to establish one. You need to share information and you also need to seek guidance occasionally. This pattern of regular reporting and discussion permits an open communication and establishes you as the leader for the team. The same principles for communication exist with an upward flow as they do to the staff. Determine what and how to communicate specific information, such as regular reporting and discussion of performance on the team and then when to report issues.

For an example, as an administrator, I would meet routinely once every week or two with the clinical managers. We would talk about staffing and survey readiness. Monthly we would discuss the financial performance of the team once the financial reports came out. They would send emails if they had a routine question or needed approval for something–such as a position to be filled, or a request for an in-service. They would call directly if they had an issue that needed immediate attention or knock on my door. These situations were more serious, such as a staff member being in a car accident, or a medication error or a compliance situation they needed guidance with.

As their boss, I felt it informed me about the teams and knew what was going on with staffing and any variances. They were overseeing what I was responsible for, and should be informed about. Being organized for these meetings really helped, and those that came to the meeting with a list of topics to discuss got more done and I viewed them as being prepared and organized. In contrast, coming to the meeting with nothing to discuss would be an issue and be perceived poorly. Seriously, there can never be nothing to discuss in this business!

Of course, every boss is different and may want different things from you when meeting one/one. Explore the expectations, but also develop a process of your own in the areas you are being held accountable for. Ensure you communicate variances, issues and concerns, but also the good things. Keep in mind that your ability to communicate the activity and outcomes of your area of responsibility is part of your performance as a clinical manager. You don't need to be career minded and thinking of promotions. It's part of doing your job and doing it well.

Being Part of the Team While Being the Boss

As a clinical manager, you exist as the head of the team you oversee, and as part of the management team. It's important to recognize this, especially if you are new to management. It's that middle zone of not being a clinician on the team, but still being part of the team. It's important for your effectiveness as a manager to keep that separation, as you are the boss.–however, work to still be viewed as part of the team by the team members.

What do I mean by that?

This is an important issue to discuss, as it relates directly back to supporting the team and assists with their overall satisfaction. Remember, it's your job to support the people that touch the patients, and that's your team. This may require an extra effort for you to accomplish this and there is a balance to maintain. The key, in my opinion, is to do this when it matters most.

For an example, if the agency had an emergency and everyone was pulling together to ensure we provided care for the patients and the staff were safe. Maybe it could be in a hurricane or a snowstorm, where everyone is rolling up their sleeves, showing up and making it all work out. It's obvious that this would be a time for management to step up and be leaders, guide the team forward and through the emergency.

It's obvious in those types of situations what managers should do. But what about a smaller scale? Those late Friday afternoons when a flurry of referrals comes in and there is not enough staff on for the weekend. It needs to be solved and could involve the clinical manager rolling up sleeves to help call around for more per diem staff. It could be a sudden staffing crunch, and a clinical manager going out for a few clinical visits.

While you may think, "of course this is the role of the clinical manager, this is what they should do." It's not always the case. I have seen 4 o'clock roll around and a clinical manager gather up their things and go home, leaving a mess for the weekend staff. I have seen a clinical manager give a staff member a ten-patient assignment, and then go out to lunch with friends.

This kind of behavior sends a message to your team, and tells them they don't matter, and you don't care. Think about how this would make you feel as a staff member. I recall the days when my boss would jump in and see patients. It made me feel like they were part of the team. I did it as well. In staffing crunches, while I didn't keep up my IV competencies and didn't know the wound care products well, I made a heck of an aide and was not afraid to jump in. It sends a message that you are all in this situation together. That the priority is the patient, and you would do what you ask of your clinical team.

There is a balance between being part of the team as well as the manager. Realize that you can't jump in all the time. You have a job to do as well. Such as needing to interview and hire candidates to fill staffing vacancies, which you can't do if out in the field all the time. It's valuable that you do jump in but balance it with your other role responsibilities or it will burn you out.

The other point I want to emphasize since I brought it up, about leaving work at 4 PM sharp. Being a clinical manager is not always an 8-hour job and you should never count on it to be that way. It's a job based on responsibility of a team, and the team is functioning 24/7/365. Sometimes you can leave right on time, but make sure your team is set and your work is done before heading out the door. Your staff are paying attention, as well as your superiors.

Being Human and Emotional

Becoming a clinical manager gave you a set of responsibilities and a role to fulfill. It did not take away your ability to be human and have feelings. However, you must have self-awareness and control of your emotions. You may get angry at a staff member and want to yell at them. But don't do it. This is especially true when you are disciplining or discussing performance issues. You need to control your emotions. Never have a conversation with a staff member when you are angry at them. Take the time to cool off and regain your balance before you meet with them. Employee matters are full of potential legal issues, and you need to ensure that your emotions are not the driver for disciplinary actions.

Yelling at staff, or raising your voice in a meeting are all ways to lose respect. They immediately view you as a hothead, or a jerk. You become unapproachable and difficult. This is not how a clinical manager should behave and is not professional. Not that you can't be human and react to situations as you would, it's your behavior from those emotions that can cause problems.

The same is true for being too nice. While some people really respond to over niceness, I have always found it to be suspicious and ungenuine. It can be viewed as being fake and lose value.

You should be yourself while at work, your genuine human self, but operating in professionally accepted boundaries. It's okay to be upset over something at work, but don't scream, yell and swear as you may at home. It's great to be nice, just be genuine about it. There are some managers/leaders that feel comfortable crying with their staff and often do when a patient dies or another tragedy strikes. But don't cry all the time.

My guidance here is to be yourself. Consider how your behavior is perceived by those around you. Are you being genuine and caring, or is it a struggle? Trust me, they know.

There are some practices I have seen that sound great at first and then lose value as they are overused. For an example, "Thanks for all you do!" Sounds nice, but it can be very overused. I always react to it because it's so general and makes me think "do you know what I do?" I find it more effective and real to thank someone specifically for something they have done or do consistently. Saying, "Thanks for picking up that extra visit today. It really helped. You are really a team player and I know I can count on you. Thank you." Rather than the generic means so much more.

In short, don't be a jerk and don't be too nice as your staff can view it as fake and lose value. Be yourself and be authentic. It will take you farther than trying to be something you're not, and having it be a challenge when you can no longer keep up the façade.

Best Practices

Being a manager is difficult. You will work hard and have a lot of demands placed on you to perform. It can take its toll on your emotional state and on how you feel like acting from moment to moment. Day in and day out, you will deal with people, coaching, teaching, guiding them to be good clinicians, stay compliant with the regulations, and to achieve performance targets. Some days this will be easy and others it will be a challenge. Developing patience helps to manage through the times when you feel challenged by staff. Take a step back, waiting a few beats before responding to an employee can help to ensure you maintain an even temperament and respectful demeanor.

Be your authentic self. Over time, you will develop your manager persona, your professional manner of being with and interacting with people at work. But don't lose who you are as a person. People will respond to you better and relate to you if you behave like a regular person, and not a robot. Share what you feel comfortable sharing about yourself and personal life. It helps people to know you better, see that you have things in common. They can see that you are human, too. Be cautious about sharing too much and talking about yourself incessantly.

Have a sense of humor. We have some crazy stuff that we deal with in home health and hospice sometimes, and some of it's funny. It's okay to laugh at work. Sometimes you just have to. Be careful to not make fun of others or staff members, laughing at situations is best. It can lighten the day and the mood.

I know I am repeating myself on this topic, but it's important to deal with underperforming staff members. Be sure to follow the rules set by your organization with personnel policies. Know them and refer to them often. When you are having trouble dealing with a difficult employee situation, use your human resources to assist and guide you.

Learn how to deal with difficult people. You have a team of independent practitioners who advocate constantly for their patients, they will advocate for themselves, and they can be a challenge to manage sometimes. But this isn't what I am referring to, it's more the problematic person and personality which you will come across and will need to learn to deal with. Build your resource chest with a periodic course or book to learn how to handle challenging personalities. You will always gain a nugget of knowledge to help you through.

Be kind and work on building your patience. No one has crowned you king or queen of your team. That's not how it works when you enter management, you just got more responsibility and a team of people looking to you to help them be successful.

Always be professional and consistent. Watch that you don't play favorites with your team members. Sometimes this can happen unconsciously, as you will have higher performers that are easier to manage than some of your staff that need more guidance and support. Treat them all courteously and well.

Mean it when you offer praise, and make sure you offer it. Make it meaningful, specific and heartfelt. Ensure your team feels appreciated. This can be a challenge as with tighter margins, salary, and benefits can be affected, pay raises may be scarce. But showing the group you appreciate them helps with retention and overall satisfaction. Be careful not to dilute it, as it will make it less meaningful. The 'personality' of your team will gauge the right balance here. Some people love to hear praise a lot, and others only want it when something extraordinary happens.

Do celebrate the wins on the team. Doing well on a survey, increasing a quality score indicator, or other measures. This engages the group in the work effort and the results and will go far in helping staff to feel involved and part of the work effort of the team.

Chapter Seven

PILLAR #5: TECHNOLOGY

TECHNOLOGY

T echnology is the last of the pillars of knowledge for the clinical manager. This pillar has the true underpinning of all the pillars and all the operations in the agency. Technology touches everything we do and has a role in every area of operations. In past years, technology took a back seat, and we completed all the documentation on paper. Implementing the OASIS documentation and the importance of outcome management pushed the evolution of technology into home health and hospice. The evolution from data entry clerks transcribing the paper OASIS assessments to point of care documentation has taken some time. Today, there are very few agencies that still do their documentation on paper.

The industry has excelled at embracing technology, leading to other operational changes such as keeping all records electronically, including scanning any paper documentation that comes into the agency. Staff roles have developed, particularly in medical records management and quality and OASIS review areas. Computer systems have streamlined processes and less staff are needed to process paperwork. This has brought data to the forefront and the ability to review trends and track outcomes by case manager.

Technology brings the need to have specialized staff or contracts with vendors to manage the software and hardware. This itself has grown from needing to manage large, heat producing servers to having the software managed virtually in the cloud. Clinical informatics positions were created in the home health and hospice space, and now these positions are specialized for the industry.

As a clinical manager, you are tasked with working with the technology available to you in your agency. There are a handful of software companies out there that serve the industry. There always is a love hate relationship with the technology from a clinical standpoint. From my experience working with all the major systems, I can tell you that not one software is perfect. They all have their challenges, and they all have little things that make them unique. The companies that have stayed around and continue to grow in home health and hospice are those who improve upon their products and listen to their customers.

It is interesting to note that most of the home health or hospice computer systems are built first to process claims. The clinical build was not first on their mind when the systems were originally conceived. This is interesting to keep in mind as you consider the clinical deficits that your software has. It was an eye-opening for me when I first considered it. Usually, the back-end billing and finance works really well, and the front-end clinical sections are clunky and require a lot of human intervention to work.

What will be interesting in the future is how the software companies will develop. The consolidation in the industry with the merger and acquisition activity directly affects the number of customers a software company has. Larger companies are buying smaller ones to grow their provider footprint across the country. Usually, the acquiring agency puts their new agencies on their platform without a second glance. So, the software that can handle and scale to accommodate large national or regional chains will be the ones to last. Over the years, there have been companies that have stopped providing software to home health and hospice agencies. I expect that there will be more as the industry evolves.

What Do You Need To Know?

Technology surrounds us, more and more of it is around us every day. As a clinical manager, you can't escape from using technology. The most successful clinical managers I have worked with have embraced technology and have worked to implement and use all the tools at their disposal. Those that struggle in this area are usually reliant on others to help them navigate their system and work to give it information.

The clinical manager is usually the staff's first contact when they are challenged with a software or other technology. That first phone call for help from the field should come your way. To be successful, you need to know your system, and you need to learn to operate in it. While you don't need to be at the level of an informatics person, having a solid understanding of the system will take you miles, reduce repetitive work and headaches.

As a manager in the organization, it is important to embrace the functionalities in the system. To do this, you need to learn it. There should be no need for an outside of the system way to keep information or documentation. While they all have some clunky processes that require some level of workaround, there should be little reason for manual processes outside of the system. *ALWAYS* do a check on yourself if you are feeling compelled to implement a process outside of the system.

Embrace and use technology to make your processes more efficient and to enhance communication, documentation, and staff satisfaction. If anytime the system is driving inefficiencies, it's time to have a hard look to ensure the process can't be done with the technology.

Software and Hardware

Software is the technology that lives within the hardware. It's the app or the program that you work on. You may not only have the main computer software in your agency, you will probably also have other applications (apps) that you will work with periodically. There are referral management software, file management software, the office or google platforms with Word™ and Excel™, Teams™, Zoom™, email, virtual visit and telemonitoring software. It surrounds you in your daily work life. Even the phone systems have software that manages calls and messaging.

Hardware is the actual physical piece of equipment. The computer on your desk is a piece of hardware with software apps installed within it. Hardware are the pieces of equipment that your staff carry around and document on. Tablets and phones are hardware that are used out in the field.

Some agencies provide their staff with the equipment needed to access the applications for documentation. Some will have a BYO or Bring Your Own model, where the apps are loaded on the staff's own equipment. There are pros and cons to each, of course. The cloud-based applications make this possible.

Servers are large computers that store the information from the application. They are usually in their own rooms, with fans and temperature controls. Many agencies have moved away from server-based programs and are using cloud-based programs. The available systems have developed this capability.

As a clinical manager, you should have a working knowledge of the hardware your staff is using in the field. This knowledge comes in handy when there are minor issues you can problem solve for them from the office. Most agencies have moved to using tablets primarily in the field. These can be easier to manage over laptops, just because of the size and complexity of the equipment. There are challenges sometimes in how easy it is to document on the tablet. Make sure you understand the challenges staff have with hardware in order to advocate for upgraded or different equipment when possible. Get involved in testing out new equipment and advocate for what the clinicians need.

Best Use Scenarios

There are so many ways to use technology to help do your job as a clinical manager. Right at your fingertips, you have access to the current patient census, the caseloads of your team, the documentation completed by the clinicians, the current schedule and even the outline of next week's schedule. Honestly, I would have killed for that 20 years ago when all of our desks were covered in clipboards. It pains me whenever I see clinical managers not taking full advantage of what their system can offer.

Best use involves using the system to bring you the information needed to make efficient and good decisions for operations. It also means that there is a commitment from all areas in the agency to use the system *in the way it was intended to be used.* All patient information should be in the system, all documentation, all outside documents such as referral information, orders, etc. All referrals should be entered and followed in the system. All of their referral documentation should get downloaded or scanned into the system and be viewable to the admitting clinician and case manager.

Referral information is often where I have seen challenges. Sometimes the detail is not easily viewed on
the admitting clinicians' tablet or they have multiple
hoops to jump through to see it. Occasionally inefficient workaround's grow up around this process, such
as printing off the referral information and having the
clinician come back to the office to pick it up prior to
the admission. This defeats the purpose of having the
information in the system and reduces efficiencies by
having a clinician spend the time running the errand. It
also has a negative impact on that clinician, adding to
the stress of their day, reducing their ability to be timely
and creates dissatisfaction all around.

Timely documentation is another best use of the
system. How often have you heard, "the numbers in the
system are different every time I run this report?" One
cause of this discrepancy is that documentation is not
being done timely. Most agencies will have policies in
place expecting documentation to be done in 24 our 48
hours, but few hold their staff to these expectations. In
order for accurate data to be available, everyone must
follow protocols. Setting the expectation that documentation be completed timely is an immense area for
clinical managers. While we all know that an admission

takes hours to complete and much of that information has to be done outside of the visit, routine visits should be completed and documented in the home. Allowing the belief and routine to be that staff document after the visits is damaging on several levels. First, that the documentation is not timely, there is a patient safety and accuracy factor regarding documenting later. Things get missed and forgotten, notes get lost, and the day eats up the energy to document everything later in the day. The other is the work-life balance for the clinical staff. They should not have to be documenting routine visits into the night.

While you may think I am dreaming about the timely documentation, I am not, and it is possible. A barrier that I have often seen with this process is that the required documentation has gotten unwieldy. Over time, agencies have a tendency to add documentation into the record to capture specific clinical data or to align with a new regulation or to fix a survey finding. There is always a lot of adding, but not a lot of taking away. Make sure the required documentation gets reviewed at least annually with a team that involves active clinicians. Focus on the visit documentation and assessments to ensure as much efficiency as possible while also meeting the regulatory requirements. With systems being developed with billing in mind, the ease of clinical documentation is an area that continues to require further development. Some systems are more progressive than others in refining the clinical areas, but most will permit some level of editing from the agency. Use it.

Another best use of technology comes from the ability to review documentation, plans of care, OASIS completion and coding all from the system. While larger agencies have a review process by Quality Assurance/OASIS reviewers and coders, all clinical managers should have a view into the plan of care established by the admitting clinicians and case managers. While your agency may have further expectations to ensure the accuracy and completeness of the plan of care/485, the software should be able to give you the insight into the care being planned and provided by the agency. Reviewing the frequency and interventions in the care plan gives insight into the planned approach and the care needs of the patient. It's here and during the case review process that the clinical manager can oversee that they meet regulations, quality of care is being delivered and the utilization of resources planned aligns with positive outcomes. The software should make this process easier by providing access and view into the documentation as soon as the clinician completes it.

Technology can also help manage the overall schedule for the agency. Everything should go into the schedule; it should be the one source of activity for the clinical teams. This means that days off, team meetings, training and all patient care services are in the system. This involves actually using the system to put the staff into it, using it as intended. Many agencies struggle with losing control over the schedule and try to use only parts of their systems, which creates other workarounds and potential for errors. As the schedule drives everything it needs to be in the system, most of the software I have worked with will not work effectively unless the schedule is used. This includes processes such as the tracking of orders and authorizations. The system won't permit another visit to be scheduled if there are no orders, which is good to comply with regulations. It also forces a MD order process in order to schedule more visits. Ensuring visits aren't completed without insurance authorization is also a good thing. We need to be paid for the care provided.

Additional benefits are using the system to track licensure and credentialing will allow the system to stop us from using staff who have failed to renew licenses. Again, protecting the agency from a survey violation and the inability to bill.

Using the system to get data is another best use for clinical managers. Easily and quickly running reports to review census, caseloads, pending referrals, non-admits, utilization and documentation completion should be a routine. At your fingertips, you have this information available to you. It may come in different forms and you may have to wait more than a few minutes for reports to generate, but all systems will have this information available to you to manage your team and have insight into patient care and outcomes and staffing needs. It's there and you have access to it. Learn how to run the reports you need to get the information, ideally you should do this independently and not relying on others to pull this data for you.

Using Tools Outside of the System

Admittedly, I have a pet peeve about not using the technology at our fingertips to manage a clinical team.

It drives me crazy to watch an agency spend hundreds of thousands of dollars on a computer system that is not fully used by the management team. Clip boards, white boards and tons of printed paper make me nuts to see when I am asked to help review operations. I understand why this is, but it still makes me cringe.

There is not one perfect system out there for home health or hospice, I can assure you. However, they all work. They all may have different strengths and weaknesses, but the bottom line is they all function. No agency is so different that a system won't work for them, but there may be a best system for an agency based on need and services. What happens in many circumstances is a lack of understanding of the processes in place and the processes needed to use the system most effectively. Gaps in implementation and training occur over time, influenced by turnover and lack of re-training. System best use is passed down from user to user, and like the game of telephone, the initial message gets mangled and bad habits and work arounds ensue. Gaps get filled in with schedules on white boards and census lists on clip boards, and everyone blaming the system.

Technology should not make our lives harder. It can change how a process works on paper to how a process will work in the system. A broken process should not continue when a system is implemented. Agencies across the country have these challenges, avoiding getting there is important. As a clinical manager, if you are considering a white board or a clip board to better manage your team, outside of the system, consider it carefully before doing it. Consider if there is a way to meet your need in the system. Work with your IT and informatics team to review the needs and what you are looking for. Connect with other agencies that use your same system to see how they do it. Have a conversation with your software vendor to see if there is something you don't know about the system. Implementing a process or a paper/clipboard/whiteboard outside of the system should be the last resort.

Home Tele-Monitoring & Virtual Visits

The public health emergency for COVID-19 prompted the Center for Medicare/Medicaid Services (CMS) to issue waivers for specific rules in home health and hospice. These should ease the overall burden on agencies during a crisis period where there were new obstacles to care, both on the patient's and clinician's side. Many patients were nervous about letting people into their homes and clinicians had limited availability due to illness. While we have could use technology to augment the care provided for years now, it has not been as widely used as it could be.

There are challenges in using technology to replace a visit to the home. There can be a lack of integration into the overall plan of care, omitting the virtual visit completely as is required. The clinician may not be aware that this was an option to consider. Often the home telemonitoring components, if large enough of a program, are completed in another team or off site, and not fully integrated into other teams. They function almost as though they were parallel programs. A remote nurse uploaded and reviewed the patient's weight, vitals and other data, and that team also dealt with any issues if they arose. The case manager can view the data, often jumping through hoops to get it in a separate app. But while the patient may have benefited from the review, they did not integrate the approach with the rest of the services, limiting the potential for further innovation. Having the two services integrated is important for care continuity and alignment of approach. This can be accomplished in various ways, such as having them engaged in case review or team meetings and addressing the data from the telemonitoring during those discussions.

With the ability to make home visits virtually renewed with the Public Health Emergency Waivers (PHE) the innovation possibilities were re-born. Using telemonitoring is proven to reduce re-hospitalization for certain diseases, but opportunities also exist for the ability for this technology to help manage patients well when challenged with staffing issues. Exploring the use of technology will help to manage in the future. It will benefit you as a clinical manager to become familiar with the potential uses at your own agency and exploring the integration with care delivery and technology. The PHE has re-awakened this interest in the industry, and I expect we will see more innovation in this area in the future.

JULIA H. MARONEY RN MHSA

Best Practices

Technology is the underpinning of operations in home health and hospice. The computer software systems are where all the patient information and visits are entered, billing is completed, and information is pulled from to manage. While it is an area I've separated as its own pillar of knowledge, it is inextricably connected to all the other pillars. Getting comfortable with and as knowledgeable as possible with the technology in use at your agency will benefit you very well.

If you are new to the computer system, learn it. Know what your clinicians know in the documentation system and get to know their frustrations in order that you can advocate for changes, updates and revisions. Getting proficient in the clinical documentation processes in the software permits you to review and guide your team to succeed both in good documentation to support the clinical care and inter-team communication, and in complying with regulations.

Learn the scheduling program in the software. While I am not saying you should do the scheduling, you should be able to jump in and revise the schedule on an as needed basis. Learning the scheduling will assist you in being able to view and manage the daily activity of your teams.

Learn to run your own reports to view caseloads, census, productivity and other areas your software may have for management. These include missed visits, documentation completion, syncing/exporting reports. Every software has recommended areas for clinical managers to review daily, weekly, etc. Being independent in running your own reports enables you to have immediate access to information when you need it, and not depend on someone else. If you run your own reports, make certain you follow a standard each time you run the report. Often, minor variations in data, such as census numbers, can occur because of requested dates or timing. Don't forget you are working in a live system with a lot of hands working in it. Things change quickly.

Explore large variances in the data. In my experience, there is usually a simple issue. I have heard, "it's always wrong" about running reports in software too many times to count and in all software. Usually the issue stems from missing an element in the report request, or people not following policy. If you have heard the phrase, 'garbage in, garbage out'? No software will fix staff not completing documentation in a timely manner, or incomplete documentation, or processes outside of the system. The software can't think on its own and anticipate needs. It has to be used as it was intended in order to deliver the information completely that is needed for operations. Often, it's the process that is causing issue, and not the software.

Ideally, your system has a clinical manager or role-based dashboard to view the data needed on a 'live' basis. These dashboards have been an evolution and in recent years, software companies have strengthened their products to offer these. Other agencies have had the capability to create them with exports to another program. The potential exists to have data at your fingertips.

Getting comfortable and competent in using technology and all software in use at your agency will benefit your success as a clinical manager.

Chapter Eight

SALES, INTAKE AND SCHEDULING PROCESSES

Sales	Intake	Scheduling
Referral Source Relationships	Processes Referrals	Assigns the Admission Visit
Cultivating Referrals	Verifies Insurance	Communicates with the Patient & Family
Facilitating Referral Processes	Gathers Patient Clinical Info	

Sales

Most home health agencies have personnel whose job is to grow referral relationships and to facilitate referrals. These positions are more numerous in highly competitive areas and agencies need them to ensure they receive referrals instead of the competition. The positions most used are sales staff who receive training in the requirements for home health and regularly visit physician offices, clinics, skilled nursing facilities and assisted living facilities. In addition, they use clinical liaisons positions in higher clinical acuity locations to facilitate referrals from these facilities. Clinical liaison staff are usually nurses, but can be other clinical professionals, such as social workers or therapists.

Hospitals typically limit the sales and liaison staff they allow into their buildings. They will require credentialing of anyone they permit onto their premises. This usually will involve health and background checks. Long gone are the days that the liaison and sales staff getting information on referrals freely by walking the corridors and building relationship with hospital discharge planners. The connections are more arm's length, or farther, and not always easy to navigate. The referral sources control them, and they will vary from location to location, even in the same town.

Relationships are key in maintaining the flow of referrals into the agency. Think about this... it is the job of the hospital discharge planner to get patients out the door and not have them return to the hospital. They view referring to home care or hospice often as enough to get the patient what they need, and the easier the agency makes the process for the discharge planner, the more likely they are to refer to that agency. Understanding that the sales and liaison staff sell 'we are easy and good'. We'll take their patients, get out to the home quickly to admit, and take good care of them so that they don't go back to the facility. That promise is directly connected to all the clinical manager handles—staffing, staff competency and good care delivery.

How an agency structures their sales teams aligns with the amount of competition in the area and the need to maintain and grow referral relationships. They need more staff in the sales area to get in front of the competition. These roles are key to growth, and to ensuring the stream of referrals continues. Without the referrals, the agency will not survive. There would not be any patients to care for!

In most home health agencies, there is little regular interaction between the clinical manager and the sales team. The sales team will largely communicate regularly with the intake department to facilitate the referral processes or to understand the reasons the clinical team did not admit a patient. The sales team works hard to bring in 'good' referrals and usually has a monetary incentive tied to the volume of admissions that occur for the organization. This is how they make their living.

Interestingly, in my experience, the clinical manager team has a love hate relationship with the sales team. They find it objectionable that the agency paid them to get referrals, and then also disliking when the referrals grow. Growth is good for the agency; however, it can be a challenge to staff for growth. Nurses in my generation, at least, have taken a while to get used to concepts of customer service and bonus pay for referrals. It's time we got over it. In these times, ensuring referrals continue or grow is vital to the overall survival of the agency. Repeat after me—growth is good!

Knowing and working with the sales team to understand their plans to achieve growth targets can be helpful in planning on staffing surges or specialty care. For example, if the sales team plans on targeting the new in town orthopedic surgeon group, this may be helpful in considering staffing needs. Knowing this strategy and the potential staffing impact to can be very helpful in planning. Having a plan to meet any surges avoids a lot of stress and craziness trying to staff for it and to meet the expectations of the new referral source.

Ideally, the clinical manager and the sales teams should work together to solve problems with 'bad', not admitted or difficult patients. The sales and liaison teams are in front of the referral sources daily, and they have a relationship with them. They have to manage the expectation of the referral source, such as why the agency chose to not admit a patient. This relationship continues with patients that are already on service and may have had a bad outcome of having to be re-admitted to the hospital. Communicating with the referral source can be very helpful to the clinical manager. While there may not be a routine need, it's a valuable source to tap into when there is a need to communicate. The sales team are front and center boots on the ground in the MD's office.

The sales team may look to the clinical manager role to assist them in understanding the regulations in home health. Often the skilled need or the homebound requirement can trip up the sales staff. Agencies need to train the sales team adequately to ensure they are knowledgeable about the rules that impact referrals.

Understanding your data regarding referrals and conversions for your team is important. Rest assured, your sales team is reviewing this information. Conversion is the number of referrals that converted into an admission. This is measured simply:

- Conversion rate% = Admissions divided by referrals.

  ○ 80% = 80 admission/100 referrals

Knowing your team's non-admit reasons and tracking this data routinely can highlight areas that need your attention. Tracking and trending non-admits by reason, and by staff, can be enlightening. Reasons for non-admission for such as homebound or no skilled need can highlight a need for re-education with staff if they trend high. Tracking non-admissions by nurse/therapist can also reveal trends that highlight a need to drill down further with staff behavior—such as non-admits on Friday afternoons. I can tell you many a story about such intel, such as the nurse who never admitted patients on sunny summer afternoons and was seen often taking a swim in the lake in the early afternoon hours on those same days. Coincidence? Maybe not, especially after several non-admits were re-referred after a visit to the ER. Data can shed light and tell a lot of stories.

Considerations for the Clinical Manager

Develop a relationship with the sales staff that works most of the referrals to your team. This can assist both parties in meeting the needs of the referral sources and establish a rapport for when issues arise. Develop a manner of regular communication. This can involve reviewing cases that were not admitted and the plan for follow-up.

Review the conversion rate for your team and the reasons for non-admit routinely. Establish a baseline for your team and understand reasons a patient is not admitted. Knowing the historical performance of the data, such as the % of non-admits, or the % reasons non-admitted can help to identify when something changes. Ideally, reviewing the records of non-admits can shed further light on why patients aren't being admitted. Agencies that are experiencing challenges with this often will have staff call the manager after a non-admit reviewing the case and the decision-making.

Intake

Intake of the referral is the next step in the usual processes. This step involves the gathering of patient information to move the referral along. Speed and accuracy here are paramount to the prevention of re-work for the clinical team. I am not a fan of re-work in any form, so I stress that accuracy here is vital. Data entering demographics and verifying insurance coverage are the primary tasks for an intake department. This may sound pretty simple, but there are challenges along the way.

Agencies staff most intake departments with a combination of clerical folks who split data entry and referral gathering tasks, and insurance tasks. In addition, there are clinicians in the department, typically LPN/LVN, or RN staff. Their role is to verify orders and essentially button up the referral for the admitting teams, ensuring that the clinician has what they need to admit.

Getting the referral in the intake department is a largely automated process. Most referrals in home health are coming in via an electronic means. This can be in a hospital system that the intake team has access to, or a referral 'grabbing' system where the intake team needs to accept a referral (prior to the competition getting to it first). There are also e-faxes, regular faxes and phone calls. Phone calls are rarer in these days for referrals, but the sales teams can call the intake department several times daily to verify the status of referrals they have been working. On occasion, a MD office may call directly to move a referral along.

Again, with the smaller agencies, often this process may be the responsibility of a few designated people in the office (including the clinical manager) or in larger agencies can be a huge, centralized department that handles all referrals. Intake is a busy department, with the goal of getting the information to move the referral along quickly for attention from the clinical team. In the past few years, technology has really helped in the intake arena, with more solutions in development. These include the ability to auto import a referral from a referral source software or e-fax, directly into the agency's software using a CCD (Coordination of Care Document). This reduces the human error elements and improves processing times, as the intake staff would need to verify the information instead of data entering the information.

The steps to verify insurance have improved with the help of technology. In the olden days, agencies would need to make a phone call to verify benefits, often being on hold for hours at a time; very inefficient. Now many agency software systems connect in the background to data clearinghouses that can automatically check that the patient has the insurance the referral source says they do. This is really easy for traditional Medicare coverage verification, but the rise of managed Medicare plans has complicated the process requiring a verification and authorization process as with the other commercial insurances.

I want to point out the differences between insurance verification versus insurance authorization. Verifying insurance means just that. The insurance coverage that the patient has gets validated. Getting authorization for insurances that require it is yet another step. This can happen in several ways and is controlled by the insurance company itself. For example, a Blue Cross plan in your area may permit one paid nursing visit prior to the need to get further authorization for more visits. Here, intake would verify insurance, and likely send the referral on to be scheduled for the initial visit. However, if the Blue Cross plan required authorization prior to admission, the staff would obtain it before the referral went to scheduling.

After the admission, if the patient requires further insurance authorizations, the same group that did the initial authorizations would manage this process or it will go to either revenue cycle staff or the clinical teams. This process is ripe for challenges. How it's completed will vary by agency. The clinical manager has a role in this process, ensuring the clinical team is not providing visits without insurance authorization is very important. Otherwise, the agency would provide services for free–being unable to be paid for not getting the authorization, which can be detrimental to the survival of the agency.

Usually, the verification and authorization process is driven by the complexities of the insurance carriers in the agency's demographic area. The more the agency has to get authorizations to cover care, the more complex the process. The software used also drives the processes. As technology has developed and is more widely used in home health agencies, it has become less people-driven and more automated. It is still a complex process that requires all hands-on deck approach, as it involves a collaboration between the clinical team and the revenue cycle teams—and each insurance will have its own nuances.

Over my career I have heard and seen a lot, but one constant is always that push and pull with the intake department and the clinical team. Resolving issues that arise between the departments is necessary to smooth the process and ensure that clinicians can seamlessly admit patients. Correct information, orders, medications, and clinical information are vital for the clinician. Often, the challenges arise because of the information provided by the referral source, such as incorrect address or phone numbers. While an incorrect address doesn't cause delays in care in a physician's office or a hospital, it can translate to a patient not being found for care to be delivered in home health.

Considerations for the Clinical Manager

Establish a connection to the Intake department. This could be with the manager or the staff member assigned to your area. Develop a rapport with these individuals to ease the conversation you may need to have to address any issues that arise. Meeting or talking regularly to review issues or concerns will help to resolve process issues. Having a level of insight into the work of the intake department can be helpful. If your clinicians are complaining about the completeness of referral information or incorrect data, already having a relationship with the leadership in the department can assist to facilitate the discussion and problem solving. Understanding their challenges with insurance companies can also offer insight into reasons for delays or opportunities to problem solve with the intake department to address them.

Scheduling

Scheduling drives everything in the agency. This is the coordination of people to patients, getting the staff front and center to do the most important part of their job, taking care of patients. Scheduling is also where the clinical manager needs to spend a lot of oversight time to ensure patients are being seen and the staff are being used effectively and efficiently.

The scheduling process really begins in the referral gathering stage. Determining when the patient will be home and available for admission can start right in the hospital, nursing home, or MD office. Communicating this information can be a challenge. The process through the referral gathering and data entry to the admitting clinician has so many unseen steps that carrying through the patient's desired time or day for a visit is miraculous.

Ongoing scheduling processes, the day to day of getting patients seen, is another driver for the agency. The matching of clinician to patient can be an art form, considering the staff schedules, the patient needs, and orders/plan of care.

Assigning the admitting clinician to the patient can be done in varied ways. Often in home health, the patient gets assigned to the RN or therapist if they work that day that in the patient's geographical area. Some agencies will plan and have people designated on the team to perform the admission. How the admission gets assigned to the admitting clinician can have a cascading impact on the rest of operations. For example, moving patients from the schedule of the admitting clinician to be seen by others on the team, moves patients around affecting the continuity, and impacts the efficiency and effectiveness of the patient care processes if the RN or therapist had a plan for that patient that day.

Scheduling is not just filling the holes on the schedule or juggling slots to fill in new admissions, it drives the plan of care, the service and the outcomes for patients. It drives how efficiently we use the staff in what they need to accomplish for the patients, and for the agency. The process of scheduling needs to consider the actual care delivery in the patient's homes, driving to and from the patient, and documentation to support services and billing.

Considerations for the Clinical Manager

The clinical manager has a huge role in scheduling as it drives the activity for the team. Oversight of the process will ensure that it is being completed in a manner that meets the clinical need, as well as efficiency for the agency. Ideally, the scheduling responsibility is completed by the team assistant role that reports directly to you, scheduling the initial and ongoing care. Sometimes this is not the case, however it doesn't excuse your oversight responsibilities. Ensure that there is a daily plan in place for taking admissions. This can be done by designating days where clinicians will be assigned them in their team or by other methods that allow for flexibility in the RN or PT's schedules. Look for patterns in your admissions data, such as the days and numbers of admissions that come in on average in a day. Make a plan to accommodate them in the schedule. While it can get crazy to schedule the visits that need to be done, a little forethought can make the whole process much smoother.

Chapter Nine

THE CARE TEAM

Plan of Care	OASIS Review	ICD 10
Establishing a Plan of Care to meet the patient's clinical needs (Orders, Frequencies, Modalities)	Review of OASIS Verifies Accuracy Ensures Consistency to Clinical Picture	Verifies Coding Accuracy Sequences Diagnosis Codes

T he care team is where much happens all day, every day. This is your bread and butter as a clinical manager. This is your home plate. Following the admission to the agency where the patient is assessed and admitted to service, several very important steps take place to establish the patient's admission, begin the plan of care, and set up billing for the care rendered.

The admitting clinician establishes eligibility, assesses the patient for clinical need, explains services and has the patient sign consents and implements orders from the referral. Combining all these elements, they contact the physician to review the initial plan of care, developing the initial visit frequencies and interventions/care modalities for that individual patient. They also must coordinate with other services ordered for the patient on the initial referral or get orders for additional services and supplies as needed (aides, therapies, social workers, etc.). Making sure they all appear on the plan of care/485 for the patient.

The admitting clinician must complete the admitting assessment and the OASIS (the Outcome Assessment Information Set) and determine the ICD10 codes for the patient diagnosis. Home health services are driven by the primary reason the patient is on services. It should reflect this in the plan of care with interventions and goals. The accurate completion of the OASIS is paramount as it affects the clinical outcome ratings and the reimbursement for the agency. No pressure or anything! It's important that the clinician get the information from the patient assessment accurately and as was intended by the tool. Remember, it is an assessment, not an interview. No amount of review and corrections after the fact will make as much of an impact as doing it right the first time. Ensuring your staff are competent in OASIS assessment is your role as their manager and can have an enormous impact on agency performance.

I want to land this as an important note, as we consider looking at the efficiencies and the effectiveness of staff's time. There is a lot that happens on that admission visit, not just for the agency in setting the stage to get things right for reimbursement and plan of care. But for the patient and their family, that first contact with the admitting clinician can set the stage for how the overall agency is perceived. Customer satisfaction is paramount, adding to the overall pressure of this visit. CMS publicly reports patient satisfaction scores along with the quality outcomes scores.

After the admission visit, several important processes happen. Depending on the size and structure of the organization, these processes are done with the clinical manager, sent to another department/position, or outsourced to an outsourced coding/OASIS review company.

- The review of the plan of care

- ICD-10 coding review

- OASIS validation review

Plan of Care/485

Ideally, the clinical manager is reviewing the plan of care for the new patient (as well as recertification and during case reviews) to ensure that the plan of care is reasonable for the patient's presentation and clinical need. Overseeing that the admitting clinician's plan for the patient is reasonable and will move the patient to having a good clinical outcome is a huge part of the role of clinical manager. This provides the patient with a second set of eyes for their plan of care. Ensuring that it meets the clinical need with frequencies, duration and services/modalities to be provided. It's here that the clinical manager can suggest changes while reviewing the clinical approach for the patient.

The clinical manager can also review the technical requirements for the plan of care/485 at the same time. However, it is my preference that this expert review be done by whomever is reviewing the OASIS. Most software systems prompt the user to complete the required elements of the plan of care/485 so the review is not as though the original was handwritten as they were prior to wide use of software. I hand wrote my first

485. The clinical manager should be able to identify what is missing from the plan of care, however, due to the software, these plans are pages long to meet all the regulatory requirements. Make sure that the plan is focuses on the patient needs and has interventions and goals.

OASIS

The review of the OASIS to ensure accuracy is vital. As mentioned, this document drives both reimbursement and quality measures, which are publicly reported and impact value-based purchasing measures (VBP). Ensuring that it's correct prior to submitting to the state and creating the Home Health Resource Group (HHRG) for payment can affect the overall health of the organization.

The OASIS is not a tool that is easy to use out of the box, and all staff that complete and review the tool need to have training. I recommend that the agency minimally provide training annually and throughout the year. With the tools changing, and turnover being high nation-wide and value based purchasing being implemented, it's vital that anyone in the tool knows how to use it accurately. Certification or the equivalent training in OASIS should be required of anyone who is reviewing it internally or externally. This assures consistency in application, instruction and corrections with the clinicians.

The OASIS review process occurs once the clinician indicates they completed documentation. This sign can occur a few ways and does not always mean that the assessing clinician 'hits a button' to notify the review team that their documentation is ready for review. Some software has this capacity in some form or the review team pulls reports to identify records completed after admission.

The reviewers will validate the OASIS documentation. This means a lot of steps and there is not an industry specific standard. However, the record is reviewed to ensure consistency in answers in the clinical record to answers on the assessment tool. Reviewers typically give focus to the questions that generate the revenue codes in the HHRG. But the reviewers pay attention to the accuracy of documentation, such as levels of assistance needed, and ability to care for oneself.

ICD 10 Coding

Using ICD-10 coding is required by the agency and will drive the overall payment category for the agency. Coding is very complex and should only be done by individuals who are certified and trained in coding. While most agencies allow the clinical staff to select the diagnoses codes, and some software systems require that at least one code be selected in order for the documentation to flow, there still needs to be a second set of eyes on these codes.

Accurate coding is driven by official coding guidelines. Up coding to capture more revenue violates these guidelines and places payments at risk inclusive of monetary penalties, including being excluded from Medicare, can be involved. So it's a big deal to do it right.

Most agencies will have an internal role that reviews the OASIS and ICD10 codes, as well as the 485. Some agencies outsource this work to an outside company to review, usually just the OASIS and the coding. I am not in favor of the role being placed on the clinical manager. This would create a need for the clinical manager to make the time and be an expert in another area. Not an efficient use of time, and pulls the clinical manager away from managing the team.

I will say that I am a certified coder. I use it when I audit records. It's a complex task. The coding book that we all reference is about 4 inches thick and weighs about 20 pounds... I may exaggerate a bit, but there is a lot to know to code accurately. With needing to be competent in the five pillars, regulations, clinical care, finance, people and technology, you'll see that there is not room in the hours of the day for the clinical manager to be doing the coding and OASIS review.

Ongoing Workflow

The workflow for the clinical teams follows this flow for new and recertified patients. A similar flow occurs for the day-to-day work of the clinical manager; scheduling, caseload management, and caseload review, managing staff documentation completion, coaching and counseling staff in their roles, assuring competency, following up on billing questions, calling patients/families, calling physician offices, coordinating with sales/liaisons on complex admissions, scheduling weekends/on-call, managing timesheets/payroll/time off requests. There is never a quiet moment!

Considerations for the Clinical Manager

Scheduling drives everything in the agency, and it's here that the clinical manager should place a lot of attention. This is where visit frequencies are met, orders are followed, care is delivered, and we achieve care continuity. If you have 5 different nurses visiting patients and they are seen on average 8 to 10 times in a 60 day episode, the outcomes and patient satisfaction will be compromised and the staff will not be happy. It is a challenge when not adequately staffed to achieve this, however its possible most of the time.

In my experience if the clinical manager for the team does not oversee the scheduling process, it becomes a hole filling exercise. The scheduler, because of the direction to ensure every one has five or six visits on their schedule every day, will fill everyone up, without regard to continuity, patient need or admissions that may come in the door. There is a balance to be gained here, and it is an art and a science. I can easily say that very few days will go the way you planned them for a schedule!

Ideally, the agency is using a self-scheduling model in which the case manager can schedule with a patient based on the patient's needs. Or ideally, if an RN is paired with a LPN, or a PT with a PTA, they can move a visit to their teammate to see. The focus in this process is patient need, following the plan of care, and continuity. Oversight of the schedule by the scheduler and clinical manager is to assign new admissions, ensure appropriate use of staff, productivity and authorizations.

The other vital area of success is the case review. While many agencies rely on their home health team case reviews, it's imperative that the clinical manager review caseloads one/one with case managers. This is especially important when there are new inexperienced staff, or new to home health staff. This permits a review of plans of care, outcomes, discharge plans, eligibility, insurance coverage/, etc. You can achieve a lot with these regular meetings and you can conduct them over the phone. Staying up on what the team is doing, their educational needs, their challenges, and what you can do to help them is an enormous factor in their success and yours as a manager. I am always surprised when this is not being done at agencies. The insight it can give is huge, and the staff value your input.

The case review is also an opportunity to review compliance with the team. Are the Medicare patients skilled, homebound, and are they remaining skilled when being re-certified? It's advisable to be looking at the records of the patients while reviewing with the staff member. This permits a quick review of the documentation to view timeliness and completion. Are the notes reflecting patient need and intervention by an MD or connection to other services?

As you review cases with the clinicians, some will stick in your mind and be familiar, others will require a review to ensure you are familiar with them. While it's not possible to know all the patients on your team, you can get a working knowledge of them. This helps when considering caseload management. What patients are more complex and take longer time? As you review, make note of records you want to review to ensure the documentation is matching what the clinician is saying for skill and medical necessity. I'm not saying you need to audit records formally during this process, and I wouldn't recommend it. But having knowledge of the patients on the caseloads is helpful in ensuring compliance. Aligning what you are hearing in the review to what they document in the record is important. Often documentation can look generic visit to visit. It's important that it be patient specific to support the needs of the patients.

The clinical manager should also be engaged in the processes and timeliness of the clinical documentation completion with the OASIS and coding review processes. If using an external review agency, ensuring that staff are following up with the suggestions in the reviews, and questions are being answered by the staff. Moving the process along with accuracy is the focus. Obtain reports, if possible, from the reviewers to identify any training needs with your team, and follow-up with new employees to ensure they are learning the documentation appropriately. If your agency is outsourcing, most companies can provide insight or reports for the clinicians on your team for comparison with timeliness and accuracy. Internal processes would have the same ability, without the reports, to account for your team's performance and timeliness with documentation.

Documentation drives everything in home health, recognize that this accuracy is part of the job. Teaching and training are important to ensure correctness and to manage risk to the agency. It's also important to carry that forward. If a staff member can't perform in this area, it affects the entire organization. As a clinical manager, you need to deal with this issue with staff, up to and including termination. It's serious when staff are not doing what they need to in the records, the agency is at risk for payment, quality and compliance with regulation. Don't take this issue lightly when staff can't perform.

Chapter Ten

BUSINESS PROCESSES

Revenue Cycle	Payroll & Accounts Payable	Finance
Cycle from Intake to Billing	Time Keeping	Budgeting
Authorizations	Verifies Accuracy	Reporting Variances
Timely Documentation	Ensures Correct Payment to Vendors & Staff	Key Performance Indicators
Collaborative Problem Solving		

Revenue Cycle

The revenue cycle is the process from intake to billing, which can be commonly referred to as the billing cycle or just plain old 'billing'. Essentially, this is where the agency submits claims for reimbursement to Medicare and other payors. The clinical manager has oversight for many of the steps in the revenue cycle and can influence how well the process is functioning for the organization.

It's vital that you understand how this works for your agency and what you can do to influence the effectiveness of the process. This can also be a process full of challenges if you don't fully understand what the pitfalls are. Often, because of misunderstandings, there are rifts between billing and the clinical teams. In my travels as a consultant, I saw this time and time again. Most of the disputes were because of a lack of understanding of what the barriers are in each department in getting the work done. Billers want to bill and clinicians want to see patients. Clinicians have a tendency to put the patient first and will try to circumvent barriers in order to get the patient what they need. Whereas the billing folks end up holding onto claims that cannot be billed entirely or are lacking information to process. The holds usually need something from the clinical team in order to move it forward.

Understand that the billing is at the end of a very long process through the agency, going from sales, to intake, to clinical, to OASIS/coding review, to plan of care review, through periods of care and then finally to the biller. These many steps and as many requirements to be fulfilled for claims to be billable, can cause a lot of error. Usually, the software systems will run the claims through a series of pre-billing checks, taking the place of a human needing to review each criterion. This includes ensuring orders and the Plans of Care (POC) are back signed, the face to face gets processed, clinical documentation is completed, and the OASIS has been completed and submitted. If the checks run into an error that requires human intervention, then the biller needs to problem solve to get the claim to process. Often, this involves working directly with the clinical team to determine whether correcting or getting the missing element is possible.

Perhaps you have already engaged in this process in your career. Often it can involve tracking down a physician to sign orders or getting a clinician to complete their documentation. Sometimes the issues are easily resolved, other times they can be more challenging. They will always reveal a potential glitch. Sometimes these are minor, and one offs, and don't require a full process change. Other times, they can show a process that has broken and requires a remedy. It's important that the clinical management team be engaged. Your familiarity with the processes can help identify the cause of the inability to bill. Your authority over the clinical team to correct their errors also helps resolve bill holds, as they often will not respond to a billing clerk's requests to complete documentation, but they will when their boss is involved.

This process should be a partnership between clinical management and revenue cycle. It should never be a contentious push and pull between clinical and finance. The divide between the two departments should not exist. Gone are the days where agencies have the luxury of fostering these dramas. It will benefit your career as a clinical manager to not foster that kind of conflict. Everyone at the agency is just trying to do their job, and the billing department does not have the insight or the authority to resolve a lot of the issues that arise. It's you as the clinical manager that has both the authority and insight, and is pivotal to resolving the issues.

Meeting routinely with the revenue cycle team will help to identify and resolve issues as they arise. This will also offer insight into what works well for your team and what doesn't. While you may tolerate a clinician who is routinely late with their documentation on the clinical side, you may find it causes holy terror in billing. Much gets revealed in this process, and I have always found it to be very educational to sit down and review an unbilled report. Trends become clear, and problems exposed.

Establishing a partnership with the business team is beneficial in working collaboratively to solve issues. Having a routine meeting and an open communication will help eliminate the rift that can occur between the departments. It will help you in identifying issues on the team in both process and person, and it will help you gain a better understanding of the revenue cycle overall.

Payroll & Accounts Payable

Payroll is something you will be engaged in at some level as a clinical manager. This can involve approving timesheets and the use of time off. Agencies do this differently across the country and from agency to agency. Sometimes you will be actually signing off paper time sheets, other times you may approve these areas in a software on your computer. This review can include the actual time and mileage for your team. You'll have insight into the miles driven, and any overtime or on-call time that the staff are doing. During this process, you may also be reviewing productivity reports. Some agencies produce these for each payroll. It's ideal to review the visit activity compared to payroll hours and mileage.

This process always involves a time crunch. Payroll has to be processed by a certain time in order to issue checks or electronic payments to the employees' accounts for direct deposit. It's always a flurry of activity and stress involved in this process from the clinical end. The timeliness of your team in getting their documentation done is again revealed. That is, if your agency ties your payroll process to the clinical documentation system, or if you are paying staff by the visit.

Over time, this process has become less arduous. However, it also means that it may have become more technical. Many agencies have turned to use a Human Resource System (HRS) software to help manage all the staff requirements and payroll. Outsourcing the actual payroll processing and payment has become widely popular with ADP™ or Paychex™ type services that manage much of the back-office processes. But the approval and oversight of the clinical manager is still required in all of them!

Accounts payable (AP) is another area clinical managers get involved in, less so in home health than in hospice. This can involve paying mileage outside of payroll, which some agencies do. It can also involve the payment and reimbursement of educational programs and conferences or other expenses that staff may incur. It may be your role to approve the payment for the team as needed, or your boss may handle this. Either way, the AP process is the paying of bills for the agency outside of payroll. Besides the clinical areas, the agency needs to pay rent or mortgages, utilities, insurance and taxes, to name a few typical categories. It is a business, and these expenses are being incurred. The largest expense, as mentioned previously, is that of the payroll, which is typically 70- 75% of the expenses incurred for the organization.

Timeliness and accuracy are on the docket for the clinical manager with payroll and any AP. Making sure that you are meeting the deadlines associated with these processes is vital, particularly with payroll. You must pay your staff and pay them correctly. Not doing so will cause unhappy staff and can influence turnover. In addition, if you are approving AP, outside vendors need to be paid in order to provide services. Slow payments from customers can damage relationships.

Finance

Interactions with the finance processes in your agency may be variable from the clinical manager role. Budgeting is one of the annual timelines in which you may have a lot of interaction. The process for budgeting typically occurs months ahead of the effective date of the budget. For fiscal years that begin in January, many organizations are budgeting late in the third quarter, in late August and September. While it takes time to compile and predict the budget, there are usually multiple approval processes that the organization must go through. These may include a board approval process, which is typically the finance committee and then to the full board. If privately owned, the processes may look similar or could just involve owner approval. The goal of the process is to get it completed and approved well before the budget is effective. Remember, the budget is the overall plan for the upcoming year. It's important that the plan be in place before it's effective and communicated to the management team. In your role, you need to know what financial indicators the leadership will hold you accountable for achieving.

The other finance process which affects the clinical manager is the monthly or quarterly runs of the financial reports. These reports show the financial performance of the agency and examine the performance to budget. These can show the need for negative variance interventions. Depending on your organization, you may receive copies of the financial statements or reports on how your team is performing. These reports typically follow the same cadence as the financial statements; monthly or quarterly.

With the financial statements, typically, Key Performance Indicators (KPIs) are included to monitor the overall performance of the agency to benchmarks, to budget or compared to targets set during the budget process. Some organizations report these in aggregate, bunching together all the clinical team results. Others can break them out, with each team having their own finance and KPI report. In my experience, having the drilled down report for each clinical team is helpful for clinical managers. You can focus on what is specifically occurring on your team, and where you have direct influence, instead of having all the reports bundled together.

It's important for the clinical manager to respond and to make a plan for action when there is a negative variance in performance. Ideally, this would have been expected by the ongoing data reviewed every day. For example, if the weekly or bi-weekly productivity reports are not up to the target each week. It will influence the financial status and can reflect as spending more money on staffing than what was expected, or bring over budget in staffing costs. Addressing this, as well as any other, would be important to align.

As a new clinical manager, or even one that is seasoned, when reviewing the financial statements or KPI reports, if you are unsure in any way what the next steps should be you need to review it with your boss or better with the finance department. This ensures that you are reviewing the information appropriately, not making abrupt and damaging changes that may have a more adverse impact later on. Such as pressuring brand-new employees to achieve the productivity standard before they are ready and fully oriented to the role. Your focus would likely result in poor morale and more turn-over, and incomplete and inaccurate documentation. Whereas realizing the new employees caused the variance and knowing it would correct itself once they completed orientation and were productive. Staying the course in this circumstance would be the best action.

Often you find that there is a fine science to balance financial pressures with the needs and functions of the clinical team. As a new manager, this balance is something you need to be aware of and learn to work with. Acting without full consideration of the impact you may cause can create a larger problem than the one you were trying to fix. Often there is not one easy or right solution to the problem. Understanding the causes of the variances is important in order to correct them.

Considerations for the Clinical Manager

Sometimes it can feel like a game of whack-a-mole for trying to strategize how to change a negative variance in your financial status. If you do one thing, it can cause other issues and so forth. To be successful at managing within a budget or to a KPI needs to begin with an understanding of the measure and understanding what caused the issue. This drill down needs to happen before deciding on changing practice or processes and is an area that many managers shy away from. The resistance is often due to lack of knowledge in how to assess the issue or lack of resources/skill to do so.

Never make a decision for your team or for your organization, without first understanding the details. Shooting from the hip to solve a problem almost always results in unintended consequences. Take the time, depending on the urgency of the situation, to drill into the causes of the problem. You could consider a financial statement or a KPI report as you would a clinical finding. A patient has pain, so what causes the pain? Is it something acute that can be resolved by taking a pain pill, is it something chronic that needs ongoing management/intervention, or is it a heart attack that needs you to call 911? Not taking the time to understand the details can cause another problem or make the current problem worse.

Once I was being influenced by unhappy nurses to hire a team to handle the on-call, as they were tired of being called out in the night to attend patient deaths. It affected their ability to work the next day and had a detrimental effect on their work-life balance. I listened wholeheartedly to their impassioned pleas and reasons and they had me almost convinced to do it. It would have meant to hire another shift of nurses, which was costly for our very narrow margin. But what was I to do? The nurses were unhappy and would likely look elsewhere for employment if I didn't take action. I was convinced until I looked at the data.

Together with my teammates in the finance department, we drilled into the data for the on-call activity to see how many triage calls and death visits were happening over a period. What we found was very interesting. In the past two years, we identified that there was an average of 1 on-call death visit every 3 months (11 PM to 7 AM). In the most recent two months, there had been a cluster of three visits during the overnight hours.

Additional review showed that it was the same nurse that had attended all three visits. It was also the same nurse who was most vocal about the issue and had led the group that was lobbying for this change. Further review of the on-call rotation showed the same nurse had switched her rotation to accommodate a personal need, resulting in more frequent on-call rotation. She would not have been scheduled ordinarily on a rotation so close together.

The data was not reflecting that there was a need to hire a team to cover the on-call overnight visits. We would have been paying them a salary every night to sit home, except for once every three months on average. It was a luxury. While appealing to the staff to not have to go out on call, it was not a reasonable cost to incur to solve an issue that clearly was a fluke. We solved the dissatisfaction by adding a hearty bonus for a nurse attending any on-call visits after 11PM. It was much cheaper than hiring a salaried on-call team to cover that timeframe and solved the dissatisfaction raised by the staff. It didn't take away the need to cover on-call, but it made it feel better both in the additional compensation and the attention of management. We also reviewed the findings with the staff to support our decision.

Don't be afraid of the numbers and what you may find as you dig into an area. Tap into your peers in the finance and revenue cycle areas to assist you in digging into the data. Be collaborative to work with as you operate in your position with the business operations. Having an attitude that you are both on the same team will carry you far and gain you the reputation of being easy to work with. Remember that success is a team sport. You will never succeed if the people around you are unsuccessful. The business operations cannot succeed without the full engagement of the clinical operations, and vice versa.

Chapter Eleven

QUALITY & COMPLIANCE PROCESSES

Quality	Compliance
Performance Improvement	Conditions of Payment
Education	Auditing
Survey Readiness	Government Reviews

The processes which support quality and compliance will often involve the clinical manager. Most of the processes involve the review of clinical record documentation to assess a variance in quality outcomes, or to assess compliance with regulation, and the conditions of payment. In many organizations, different departments and different individuals have oversight in these areas. However, when they converge at the clinical manager level, the activities for each area are very similar and can overlap, as the clinical manager has responsibility and oversight for the quality of care and compliance with regulation.

Quality

Record Audits

With value-based purchasing (VBP) and its expansion into all home health agencies across the country in 2023, it becomes even more vital that a clinical manager understand the measures and how the clinical care and documentation affects them. Typically, there is a quality coordinator or other position in charge of the overall activity. In larger agencies, this can involve having an entire department overseeing multiple agencies across the country.

The activity to review the clinical data is usually as a focused audit. This helps drill down to understand why the performance measure is not up to the benchmark or to the goal set by the agency. The focus would usually be to gather data to assess what needs to change in order to improve the overall scoring. The clinical manager would usually have a level of responsibility to review the records and complete the overall audit form to ensure that the clinical documentation meets the agency's standards.

For example, if the scoring on Improvement in Dyspnea was less than the state and national benchmarks, the agency could delve into the reasons this was occurring and what the care practices were at each agency or team. Through a record review, the details of each admission could determine care variations that impact outcomes. Collecting the details could show variations in practice or deviation from expected policy among some things, and guide changes to improve the measure.

Additionally, or in combination, agencies will typically have a record audit requirement within their overall Quality Assessment/Performance Improvement Plan (QAPI). Some state licensure rules require a specific % of records be reviewed each quarter to assess the quality of care and adherence to the state and federal regulations. The rules usually prescribe these as a % of the total patients seen during that period and can vary from state to state.

The most organized and effective QAPI programs will combine the audit indicators to ensure that records are reviewed to meet both purposes. Ideally, the agency can combine the reviews into one audit tool to reduce the time it takes for the overall review.

Quality Projects

Another area that clinical managers could be engaged is in is quality projects by participating or leading them. A QAPI project could involve many things, but most will focus on some aspect of care or efficiency. Typically, a lower performing area is identified. It could be measured compared to a benchmark or in an outcome report or as a complaint from a patient or family. I have always loved to dig into a quality project, mostly as it brings an opportunity to poke into data to understand the likely causes of the poor performance. Reviewing data, asking questions, reviewing actual processes with team members can be a lot of fun. It's gratifying to fix the problem and watch the improvement happen.

QAPI projects can really engage the entire team and the agency, as all levels of staff should be engaged in improving the overall processes. It really helps to engage people in their work and to establish a culture of improvement and service excellence.

There are several approaches to performance improvement, with Six Sigma and Plan, Do, Check, Act (PDCA) cycles likely the most popular. Over the past several years, agencies have adopted and tried various methods that used to only be popular in manufacturing processes. This has resulted in dramatic changes and gains in efficiencies in many organizations. Hospitals in patient throughput from the emergency room to the inpatient floors or physician office practices with their patient scheduling and reducing wait times. Home health and hospice organizations have used these methods to improve the overall efficiency of admission time and response to referrals or response time on call. There have been some dramatic results by applying the principles of quality improvement.

As a clinical manager, you may be part of a quality improvement project, or you may lead one on a smaller scale within your team or branch. It's important to be aware of the principles of the overall review process, how data is used and how to drill into the data to find the causes. This is an entire science, and there are multiple theories and practices. I've listed some resources at the end of this book for further review. Don't let the complexity of some of them deter you from participating in projects. It can be really stimulating to take part in a quality project.

Compliance

Compliance with regulations is an ongoing process and something the clinical manager oversees day in and day out. Complying with the regulations for a certification and survey standpoint means you are ensuring that the operations of your team complies with the federal and state rules for a home health agency. Some organizations, if they separate quality and compliance into two separate departments, will have one or the other oversee the activities for survey readiness. Usually, this will fall to the quality department, as they will oversee mock surveys and internal assessments to ensure compliance with these rules.

For a clinical manager, compliance activities will overlap between the conditions of participation and

the conditions for payment and are not as easily ex-
tractable. For this reason, I'm including them under the
processes of compliance together.

Surveys

A compliance review for a mock survey, where an internal manager acts as a surveyor, will mirror the activities for a true survey. Outside consulting firms also
use this method. The agency will receive a report after
the reviewers complete the survey process. Ideally, this
process closely mirrors a real survey, with reports and
areas which require management to correct.

During the actual survey, there may be standard or
conditional citations which will require a plan of correction (POC) to be completed and sent to the state
survey agency for its approval. These are areas identified on survey which are found to not comply with
the state or federal regulations. Typically, the surveyor
would find the deficiencies on record review or during
a home visit with a staff member.

The length of a survey and the number of surveyors
will depend on the size of the organization. Typically,
they last for three days. As a clinical manager, you'll

be directly involved. They will ask you to coordinate home visits and staff interaction with the surveyor. Often, the surveyors come prepared with the names of the patients they wish to visit. They obtain these through the OASIS data and may be patients with adverse outcomes identified in reports. Wound care patients and IV patients will usually get selected in order for the surveyor to observe more complex care being performed, along with other types of patients.

Organizing these home visits will be part of the clinical manager activities. The patient will be asked to grant permission for the surveyor to visit the home. In addition, the surveyors will probably take some time to interview you. They will usually have a focus, such as policy and procedure and staff education. Lately, the focus has been on the COVID response and infection control areas. If unsure, make sure you connect with whomever in the agency is organizing the surveyor. It could be the quality department or other leadership.

Preparing for survey because they can happen at any time, will be an ongoing process. The making of home visits with your team members as part of their performance evaluation fits directly into this preparation. The bag technique, infection control and handwashing are all areas in which you can guide and coach your staff to do every day, and areas in which surveyors will focus. Having prepared and trained your staff all along the way helps tremendously in this aspect. Surveys become less of a stressor when you know you're ready for them.

If your agency has a plan of correction to complete, you may be part of its development and implementation. For example, if the surveyors cited the agency that a staff member forgot to wash their hands, the plan of correction would likely include staff training and observation to be accomplished by a certain date. In the next survey, or sooner, depending on the number and seriousness of the citations, this area would be a focus for the surveyor. It's always a good practice to ensure the continued follow-up of issues noted on survey. This helps to ensure that your team fully addresses the correction and won't get cited in the next survey. Findings that are repeated on a follow-up survey or subsequent surveys are treated with a higher-level of citation, as it shows continued non-compliance and an inability to correct performance. In some circumstances, if repeated offenses are serious enough, it can place the agency's licensure and Medicare participation in jeopardy. Serious stuff!

Conditions of Payment

To assess the compliance of the agency with the Medicare conditions of payment, agencies will typically undergo an audit. This can be an internal audit, or an external review completed by a consulting firm specializing in compliance review. Ideally, the agency is conducting the audit internally to verify if there is an issue. Sometimes, if done externally by a firm, the activity is completed under attorney-client privilege to protect the agency should they find something they are doing wrong. This affords the time and review to get legal advice on the next steps to take, usually involving self-reporting the error and paying back monies to the federal government.

Performing these reviews, these audits, internally helps to identify areas of risk that re-education or process change can correct. It's ideal to know your own faults before an external audit from CMS exposes them.

An audit can be done by a contractor of CMS, either as a probe audit by the fiscal intermediary or by a specialty fraud contractor. These types of audits can bring serious consequences if they uncover areas where significant mistakes get made, or documentation does not support the services provided. This can be viewed as fraudulent billing and hefty fines along with payback of claims that should not have been billed. Agencies have gone out of business and people can get fined and jailed.

Now that I've scared you, I also want to assure you that knowing the rules and following them will help in assuring the bad stuff doesn't happen. Compliance should be an ongoing process. Make sure you and your staff are aware of the areas of risk. You should imbed identification and mitigation of risk in your day-to-day processes. The most prevalent areas include the conditions of payment; homebound, medical necessity, signed orders/plan of care, face to face, consents, etc.

Considerations for the Clinical Manager

In most agencies, the clinical manager is not leading the quality or compliance activities, but plays an important role in both. Typically, the involvement is primarily going to be in record audits, reviewing the documentation of your team. While this review should be an ongoing process as you review admissions, recertifications and caseloads, the record audits collect data for performance improvement purposes or to monitor a compliance area. They also, in the instance of state regulation, help to meet the record auditing requirements for the state.

Become familiar with the agency's performance improvement approach. You can do this by reviewing the policies and the QAPI plan, and by working on projects with the leaders in the quality departments. This will help you understand the approach and how it's applied. Understanding the methodology will assist you in knowing what to expect when a QAPI project is underway in your area and to take part more effectively.

Getting familiar with quality improvement can also help you improve performance on your teams as you coach and teach your staff. You're improving performance daily on a smaller scale than doing a large project. Knowing the approaches can assist you in building your overall knowledge and help to move your career forward. In our business, quality and performance need constant attention. This helps to adapt and change as care in the home evolves. If you choose to move onward and apply for higher-level positions, having a background in a quality or performance improvement or certification in an accepted method—like Six Sigma, will help move your career forward. Being skilled at performance improvement and using a scientific method to make positive change will put your head and shoulders over other candidates. You can use these methodologies for both the quality of care and for financial performance, very useful tools to master as you build your career.

Take to heart the statement, compliance is not an event, it's an ongoing process. In your role as a clinical manager, focus on these areas every day, all day. Ensuring your team is knowledgeable about homebound, skill and medical necessity is essential in this process. Reviewing those elements when reviewing cases, admissions and re-certifications helps to have the oversight, which is essential to success in this area. In addition, making sure that you communicate to your leadership team when there are areas which need correction or attention and should not get billed helps the agency avoid future liability.

Pay attention to risk areas in which CMS is focusing on. You can get these by reviewing the Office of Inspector General (OIG) work plan or MAC listing of finding on audits for denials. These can also involve areas defined on an internal or external audit in which the agency needs to focus. Be involved and be part of improvement processes for the agency.

Chapter Twelve

PUTTING IT ALL TOGETHER

Getting & Staying Organized

One of the most helpful things you can do for yourself as a clinical manager is to get organized and stay that way. This doesn't mean that you need to go shopping and get your desk all decked out with Martha Stewart organizational gadgets. While this all looks nice, and it can help to get things organized initially, it's unnecessary.

Being organized does not mean that you will have a neat work area or a lack of piles of paper on your desk. It's more about the overall approach to the day/week and the tasks at hand. Having a consistent, reliable approach to getting work done and responding to unplanned demands will benefit you now and into the future.

Daily Tasks

Identify for yourself what tasks require your attention every day. These can include;

- Oversight to the team schedule for the day and the week.

- Reading and responding to emails.

- Responding to daily tasks/reviews in the clinical documentation software.

- Reviewing any daily reports–missed visits, documentation, etc.

A key practice is to set a routine for when you address and complete these areas. It is more effective to address the schedule when you first arrive at the office, making sure the scheduler/team assistant is all set and all visits are assigned for the day. Then moving to reviewing any outstanding documentation, ensuring the process keeps moving forward. This could involve the review of a plan of care completed the day before, orders, or any notes you've flagged to review in your system.

Review email and address anything urgent that may impact the schedule or immediate communication needs of the clinical team. Certainly, this will involve making sure that you are addressing the urgent issues. Email can be a bear to manage, and you can waste hours daily on reading and responding to it. Set up a process where you dedicate time throughout the day to manage it. Perhaps cleaning it up one time in the morning to capture any detail that may need to be addressed from the previous day. Focusing on emails from your team and your supervisor–particularly on anything directly sent to you. I would also advise to develop a real time method of keeping or deleting emails. I am an email hoarder, keeping them until my inbox is in the thousands, and then taking a lot of time periodically to delete and keep/file. I don't advise operating this way. There are better ways to organize yourself.

It's helpful to also have a process to scan emails as they come in, to respond to anything urgently. Having email come to your phone and/or other wearable device is helpful to keep tabs on what is building up for later. This enables you to have a quick glance at your phone while in meetings, so that you are still reachable even though you are otherwise tied up. This approach requires skill and practice to do effectively and not disrupt the meeting you are in.

I wear a smart watch that vibrates each time I receive an email or text. I had to learn to not look at it every time this happens particularly when in a meeting with someone. Looking at my watch can appear to be looking at the time, and whomever I am with gets the impression that they are taking up too much of my time, not what I intended. Now I use it as a reminder to check email when the meeting is done, instead of during the meeting. You'll need to determine what works best for you and find that balance.

Your attention as a clinical manager needs to be on the need to move the documentation review process forward. How much of your time and what you review depend on the system that you use. Some systems will have a dashboard or a workflow that you need to process in order that the document flow moves forward. As discussed, the revenue cycle processes rely on the effectiveness and efficiency of these paperwork flow processes.

Establishing a daily routine for yourself helps to move the working of the agency forward. Keeps you organized by getting work accomplished and workflows processed. But it also helps to establish your reputation as a manager, in that you will take care of things and respond to communication. Your staff knows you are looking at the schedule, their email to you, or the documentation they completed yesterday. Your supervisor also knows this, and both your team and your superiors view you as reliable and capable.

Not using an organized approach and taking the day as it comes will not help you get work done, nor will it help you in your career. There is so much of the day that is out of our control and will get shuffled to deal with an immediate concern or a fire that needs putting out. It's the nature of our business. However, if you approach everything you need to do by the seat of your pants, you will accomplish nothing, and your stress level will be out of this world!

Weekly & Monthly Tasks

Review in your organization what needs to happen on a weekly basis, and plan your upcoming week, at least a week ahead of time. Identify what needs to happen for that week. This could involve meetings, payroll processing, performance reviews, caseload reviews, audits or supervisory visits that need to be completed. Schedule the time in your calendar as you would an appointment to get specific things accomplished. If you need to have payroll processed on Tuesday before noon, schedule the time and not schedule other meetings during that time.

Knowing ahead of time what your week looks like and what you need to accomplish establishes a plan for the time. Allowing time slots to get work done helps you to accomplish what needs to be done during that time frame.

You can view the same process for monthly items that need to be accomplished, meetings that are held, and processes that require your attention. Plan these out to ensure you've set the time aside to get them done.

Meetings

Meetings should be a time where a group of people get together to discuss specific agenda items and to communicate or make decisions. As a clinical manager, you are going to have meetings with your team and meetings with your superiors. For both types of meetings, it is beneficial to be prepared and be on time both for the meeting and when conducting the meeting. Building an agenda with items that need to be addressed during the meeting will assist you to stay on track and to help move others along in the conversation.

Drive the meetings with your team with a set agenda and timeframe for each area. Take the time to communicate needed information to your team and to discuss specific items, such as patient care or to review patient cases. Start on time and set the expectations with the team that all meetings will begin on time. Coach the team to be efficient and effective when communicating regarding patient care coordination. Divert them from going off on tangents or discussing areas that aren't pertinent to patient care. It's always a learning process, including for you as the manager. Sometimes the team needs an opportunity to laugh or bond over a case or an event, learn to balance these out so you get through agendas and share the needed information.

Monitoring Key Performance Indicators

Develop a process to review your team's performance for yourself that coincides with the production of the key Performance Indicators (KPI) reports from finance. Schedule in when you expect to receive them and take the time to review and understand your team's performance. This can include setting up standing meetings with a leader from the finance department and/or your supervisor to ensure you are reviewing and responding to the data appropriately. Taking this approach will enable quick attention to anything out of sync with benchmarks, budgets or goals and establish you as a proactive manager in the eyes of leadership.

If your agency has the capability, make sure that you're analyzing any kind of benchmark reports to review each of your staff's performance to the key performance indicator. This process will enable you to know which employee is performing or needs some help to get to where they need to be. This drill down to each employee also permits goal-setting and facilitates the overall performance evaluation process. By understanding each employee's performance, you will address their individual need for training and further coaching to increase productivity or address patient outcomes.

Professionalism

One thing that can really kill your career is being unprofessional. You may be the best manager performing at the highest standard, but if you are unprofessional or a jerk, you will not advance in your career and people will not want to deal with you. Upper leadership would rather deal with someone who was a charm to be around and would take a lesser performing individual if that was the choice.

As a manager, you cannot just act in any way that you please while at work. You have a role to play being a manager; you have employees that look up to you and upper management that rely on you. This responsibility can sometimes be a burden. While you would sometimes dearly love to shout obscenities at a poor performing staff member, it would be highly unprofessional. It would mark you for a very long time and the behavior would become your legend. I have worked with a manager who carried that burden of losing it somewhere along the way with a subordinate. It carried him through his 20-year career and was a legend at the water cooler gossip. It can be regrettable, I know.

I had this experience as a new manager. A very irate nurse screamed at me in the hallway after a team meeting, so everyone was there and bore witness. It was about productivity; I remember that clearly. She told me to shove it, and I replied in anger. If I recall accurately, I fired her right on the spot, in so many words. It was a terrible idea all around, and I learned a precious lesson that day. There was a lot of clean-up that needed to happen, including rescinding the termination and a series of meetings with the employee and human resources. We eventually resolved the situation, but the wound was still there and the employee eventually left. Unfortunately, the nurse was a great clinician, a truly seasoned RN, but the interpersonal was a challenge, documentation was late, and productivity was an issue.

The bottom-line was that it was a salvageable situation, and I blew it. New to the role and being challenged by difficult employee was not something I was prepared to do. I had no coach, no guide in my new management role. Learn from my mistakes. When challenged by a very emotional or volatile situation/conversation, take a step back and seek to calm the employee. Don't decide on official disciplinary action until you are both calmed down and can speak reasonably to each other. Involve human resources if you need to as an anchor in the conversation. Work to maintain a level, steady emotional state and stay calm when faced with a steamed employee. A reliable and consistent state will help you maintain your professionalism.

The other area of professionalism is the presentation. How you present yourself and the manner in which you dress makes a difference. Make sure you follow the dress code of your organization, but take it up a notch. I'm not saying you need to wear suits to work as a clinical manager, but you need to differentiate yourself from the staff and present yourself as a professional, because you are! Consider not wearing scrubs if you are not required to, at least on the days you are not in the field. While they may be very convenient, you blend into the crowd and look like part of the clinical team. As a manager, you want to stand out from the crowd. I may be old-fashioned on this note, but I can tell you from experience that it makes a difference in how people view you. If you want to advance your career, regardless of whether you want to stay in your current role or seek promotions, the manner in which you present yourself matters.

Chapter Thirteen

TAKING CARE OF YOURSELF

As a clinical manager, in a sometimes very stressful job, you need to identify when it's time to take care of yourself. We're not superhuman people, and we need to make sure that we acknowledge that. Time away from work is necessary. We need rest, nutrition and peace. Periodically stepping away from the stress of the job is necessary to maintain balance. As clinicians, we think of ourselves as superhuman, that we can take care of everybody and everything and ignore our own needs. It doesn't work that way. We're don't have an endless supply of energy and attention. And frankly, no one expects that of us. I think it's the over-achiever tendencies that lead us to drive incessantly forward. This is a common situation, especially for someone who is seeking to advance their career, or to be the best clinical manager possible. Likely, this aligns with someone like you, who has picked up this book to ensure your success.

Of course, everyone talks about the work life balance. What does that really mean when you're trying to balance family life or work life and maybe even a career advancement? Essentially, that means that you have a balance *that works for you* between your work life and your home life. You feel balanced and able to take care of things at work and also what needs to happen at home without killing yourself from overwork and lack of sleep. All of my life I have worked to achieve a work life balance, and I have failed miserably many times. It's difficult when you have a demanding job to step away from it. And sometimes you can think that you're a failure if you take time away or need to take care of yourself by taking vacations or even going to the doctor.

People nowadays seem to be more in tune with the ability to have a balance between work and home. My advice to you here is to make sure that you take the time you need for yourself. Acknowledge that you need to take time away from work, that you need to take your vacation time, that you need to take holidays off, you not need to work every weekend or work from 7am to 7pm every day. You need to have friends, pay attention to your family and have that otherwise balanced life that we all strive to have.

The thing that I learned to do after coming to terms with the fact that I wasn't very balanced in my work life and home life was to un-plug. If I wasn't on call as a manager, I would unplug my phone at night. I would leave it outside of my bedroom so I wouldn't hear it vibrate and my husband wouldn't hear it vibrate. I would make sure that my phone was in privacy mode after a certain time. My staff all learned that if they really needed me during the night, and I wasn't on call, they would call the house phone. Other than that, if I was on call, I would have my phone on and I would be available for any calls during the overnight period. If you're not on call, if you're not supposed to be working, step away from it periodically.

The other thing that I continue to do is to make sure that one day a week I didn't work and mostly that really helped. I would take either Saturday or Sunday and make sure that I stepped away from work. I wouldn't turn on the computer, didn't open emails and do things that were not really necessary. This works well for me.

Kind of gave me a fresh reset button for the week. And I could focus on more important things like friends and family instead of just what was happening at work and trying to get caught up when the office was closed.

There's also the factor in managing your emotions. One thing that you need to pay attention to is how you're responding to certain situations. Making sure that you have a level head and you keep a reliable and consistent emotional state. This includes being able to take a step back when you're confronted with controversy or a furious employee so that you don't respond in a way that's unprofessional. This can cause a huge amount of problems later on. You need to pay attention to your own emotional responses. If you're getting overly frustrated and angry about situations, it's probably time to take some time off to take a step back and reevaluate. Reassess your feelings periodically. Know what's causing your emotional reaction. Certainly in the hospice world, where there's a lot of death. Situations can become very emotional and draining after a period and you should acknowledge your own response to them. As a clinical manager, you support your team through a lot of loss and it can get daunting for you emotionally. Ensure that you're being intelligent with understanding your own emotional responses to things.

The other part of taking care of yourself is and your physical health. I am not a role model in this by any means. However, there are folks out there who have been successful staying fit and healthy and having that overall balance with their physical and nutritional needs. We have a tendency when we're very busy as clinicians to put others above ourselves. I have always had the bad habit of putting work over exercise. This certainly hasn't worked well for me and it's always a constant struggle. But there is benefit and taking a walk and taking time to make sure that you are moving your body, getting exercise and staying fit and healthy.

That same goes for having good nutrition and a good diet. As clinicians, we know what that means. It means eating more vegetables. It means not having McDonald's for lunch every day. One of the other things that I see a lot of clinical managers do is skip meals. Skipping lunch, not having a plan to have a healthy lunch, and then being so ravenous later on in the day that you're eating everything in sight. Plowing through all the cookie stashes in your desk. That doesn't help things. The sugars highs and lows don't help you with managing stress in the office.

The other thing is paying attention to your own use and abuse of drugs and alcohol. There's a tendency in clinical management and administration to have a drink or two at night or to go out with your employees. One thing that you have to be very cognizant about is balancing that for yourself. There's a lot of stress in our work and people have a tendency to imbibe too much in both drugs and alcohol in order to manage stress. Pay attention to what you're using alcohol for.

Mental health needs have reduced stigma over the past several years. Reach out when you feel as though you need help. I've known and have worked with hundreds of clinical managers across the country in the past several years. And I've seen an increase in people who have been very open about reaching out for mental health guidance and coaching as their stress levels increase over what they can effectively deal with. Reach out to resources if you find you are needing help and to talk to someone. Check into your employer offerings with Employee Assistance Programs (EAPs). These are confidential and usually very inexpensive or free.

We all should live the life we want and be a happy and balanced as human beings. Ensuring that you're balancing your work, your career goals with your human needs is vital. Remember, in the Maslow's Hierarchy of Needs, you need love and connection before you get to the overall self-actualization goals.

Chapter Fourteen

DEVELOPING YOUR WORK PLAN

The goal of this book was that you not only read and learn but also develop a personal plan for your own career growth, whether you're a new manager or your plan is to stay and grow in your current position, or if it's being the CEO of your own agency. Identifying where you need to grow and learn is the first step, and then creating a plan for how to address the areas that need attention would be next. I want to point out that no one who is an outstanding leader has ever felt they have arrived. They continue to focus on areas of professional and personal development. You should try to emulate that behavior, grow and learn, it will help you better enjoy the work and to help others.

So now what? Now that you know all the things that a clinical manager should know, how do you put it out together? How do you make yourself into a successful clinical manager?

First, realize that change is a process, and it takes focus and purpose to grow and to be the successful manager you aspire to be. It is not a matter of luck, it's a matter of working hard and purposefully toward a goal.

Take a few minutes and develop your work plan. This is your personal plan. No one else needs to look at it or review it, just you. Unless, of course, you want them too. Identify the areas that you need to work on, where you need to grow or to expand your knowledge. Go back to the five pillars to review where your focus should be. These are areas you need to have a solid foundation, start there. Where do you feel the need to expand your knowledge? Is there an area that you feel shaky about? Do you need to build up resources and references to ensure you have what you need to guide your team? Is it understanding finance or regulation? Or is it the people management aspects? Develop the plan on how you will address those areas. Will you take a course? Maybe find articles or books on the subject to help understand the issue. Could it be meeting with someone in your agency, such as the finance manager or your supervisor, to address the areas you feel you need help with? Make sure the material you get applies to home health or hospice. Some materials published widely are pretty generic. Just be sure that it meets your needs. There is not a lot out there specifically for home health or hospice operational or financial management. However, a lot of the generic applies.

Perhaps your goals include expanding your career. Is there a certification that you can aspire to achieve? Is there a promotion in your agency that you want to get? Maybe you have more defined and long-term goals you want to plot out and create a path toward. The process is the same. Develop your plan to get there. What steps do you need to take to achieve your goals?

A friend of mine once told me you have to treat your career like a business. A business is what it is. It's your life. It's your income for a long time, and you really need to reevaluate it from time to time. Once you have a work plan or a career path, you need to go back and reevaluate it periodically. Every few months, take out your work plan and review it. Determine what needs to change. Your goals may have changed. What do you need to do in order to achieve your overall target goal?

And honestly, it's okay for things to change. How many times do you change your mind about where you want to be and what you want to do in your life? It's highly relevant to change your mind periodically about where you want to go in your career. But look at what you need to learn as you adapt to your changing desires. Set up a goals and steps to meet learning needs and address those deficits that you discover. Always move forward.

Don't ever feel as though you can stop learning and stop growing. Even if you consider yourself too old or too close to retirement to change. Keep in mind that many people now live a long time after retirement. Maybe your goals change to something that you can do part time or per diem.

The most successful people in management and leadership continue to learn. They never stop. They read books; they go to conferences. They seek help; they seek coaching; they seek guidance. And that's what makes them successful. It's you that drives your own career path. It's you that drives your own education. It's you that drives your own goals. Your goals and your aspirations will differ from others. Try not to measure yourself against them as you move forward in your career. Everyone's path and careers will differ. It's all right to model certain aspects of others that you may admire. It's all part of the process of growth.

Take one step at a time, but keep moving forward!

Chapter Fifteen

RESOURCES

The Author is providing this list as a reference – is not endorsing any of the products listed, and has no relationship with them, unless otherwise stated, and cannot guarantee the links.

The Clinical Manager Source

*This is the author's website for references – offering books, courses, podcasts, and newsletters

- https://theclinicalmanagersource.com/

Refer to your own state associations and state licensing regulations as applicable

Home Health Provider Center on CMS website
- **Use this main page to access a ton of resources – get on mailing lists for updates**

- http://www.cms.gov/Center/Provider-Type/Home-Health-Agency-HHA-Center.html

Chapter 7-Medicare Benefit Policy Manual - Home Health regs:

- http://www.cms.gov/manuals/Downloads/bp10 2c07.pdf

Chapter 10 Claims Processing Manual–Home Health

- https://www.cms.gov/manuals/downloads/clm1 04c10.pdf

Interpretive Guidance

- https://www.cms.gov/Medicare/Provider-Enrol lment-and-Certification/SurveyCertificationG enInfo/Downloads/QSO18-25-HHA.pdf

Conditions of Participation (COPs)

- https://www.gpo.gov/fdsys/pkg/FR-2017-01-13/ pdf/2017-00283.pdf

- https://www.federalregister.gov/documents/20
  17/01/13/2017-00283/medicare-and-medicaid
  -program-conditions-of-participation-for-ho
  me-health-agencies

- https://www.ecfr.gov/current/title-42/chapter
  -IV/subchapter-B/part-424

- https://www.ecfr.gov/current/title-42/chapter
  -IV/subchapter-G/part-484

State Operations Manual – Home Health
- https://www.cms.gov/manuals/downloads/som
  107c02.pdf

The National Association for Home Health & Hospice Care (NAHC)
- https://www.nahc.org/

HIPAA
- https://www.hhs.gov/hipaa/for-professionals/in
  dex.html

Office of Inspector General

- https://oig.hhs.gov/

  - Look for the annual work plan sections for home health and hospice

Chapter 4 - Physician Certification and Recertification of Services Medicare General Information, Eligibility, and Entitlement

- https://www.cms.gov/manuals/downloads/ge10 1c04.pdf

The Medicare Administration Agencies (MAC)

-Each MAC is a little different – but they all offer education and resources, you CAN access these resources even though the MAC does not cover your area.

Palmetto MAC for HH + H for the following states: Alabama, Arkansas, Florida, Georgia, Illinois, Indiana, Kentucky, Louisiana, Mississippi, New Mexico, North

Carolina, Ohio, Oklahoma, South Carolina, Tennessee, and Texas

- https://www.palmettogba.com/palmetto/jmhh h.nsf/DID/9C6RZ83761

- Palmetto's Local Coverage Determinations (LCDs) (both Home Health & Hospice)

  - https://www.palmettogba.com/palmetto/jm hhh.nsf/DID/8B3RW86238

- Top Claim Denial Reasons for both Home Health & Hospice

  - https://www.palmettogba.com/palmetto/jm hhh.nsf/DID/B9KPVS3022

National Government Services (NGS) HH + H for the following states: Alaska, American Samoa, Arizona, California, Guam, Hawaii, Idaho, Michigan, Minnesota, Nevada, New Jersey, New York, Northern Mariana Islands, Oregon, Puerto Rico, US Virgin Islands, Wisconsin and Washington, Connecticut, Maine, Massachusetts, New Hampshire, Rhode Island, and Vermont

- https://www.ngsmedicare.com/web/ngs

- NGS's Local Coverage Determinations (LCDs) (both Home Health and Hospice

  o https://www.ngsmedicare.com/web/ngs/medical-policies?lob=93618&state=97282&region=93623

CGS HH + H for the following states: Delaware, District of Columbia, Colorado, Iowa, Kansas, Maryland, Missouri, Montana, Nebraska, North Dakota, Pennsylvania, South Dakota, Utah, Virginia, West Virginia, and Wyoming

- https://www.cgsmedicare.com/hhh/

- CGS Local Coverage Determinations

  o https://www.cgsmedicare.com/hhh/coverage/index.html

Medicare Compare
- https://www.medicare.gov/care-compare

OASIS

- Resources for OASIS manuals, forms and up-dates

  - https://www.cms.gov/Medicare/Quality-Init iatives-Patient-Assessment-Instruments/Ho meHealthQualityInits/HHQIOASISUserMa nual

- OASIS Answers

  - https://oasisanswers.com/

Home Health Prospective Payment – Patient-Driven Groupings Model

Scroll to the bottom of this page to check out the links to the resources offered – several with explanations including the article below

- https://www.cms.gov/Medicare/Medicare-Fee -for-Service-Payment/HomeHealthPPS/HH-P DGM

MLN Matters Number: SE19027. (2019). *Overview of the Patient Driven Groupings Model.* Department of Health & Human Services.

- https://www.cms.gov/files/document/se19027.pdf

Home Healthcare Management and Practice - Clinical and management focused research articles

- https://journals.sagepub.com/home/hhc

Home Healthcare Now

- https://shop.lww.com/Home-Healthcare-Now/p/2374-4529

Wound, Ostomy and Continence Nursing Society (WOCN)

- https://www.wocn.org/

The **Association for Professionals in Infection Control and Epidemiology (APIC)**

- https://apic.org/

VNAA Clinical Procedure Manual

- https://vnaacmssite.qa.membershipsoftware.or
g/content.asp?contentid=149

The Society for Human Resource Management

- https://www.shrm.org/

Newsletters
Home Care Week

- https://www.aapc.com/newsletter/home-care
-week/

Home Health Line

- https://homehealthline.decisionhealth.com/

Home Health Care News

- https://homehealthcarenews.com/

Six Sigma Resources
The Juran Institute

- https://www.juran.com/

Chapter Sixteen

REFERENCES

Belker, Loren B., McCormick, Jim., Topchik, Gary. *The First-Time Manager, 7th Edition*. Harper Collins Leadership, 2018

HHA Center Webpage at: http://www.cms.gov/Center/Provider-Type/Home-Health-Agency-HHA-Center.html

Marrelli, Tina. *The Nurse Manager's Survival Guide, 4th Edition*. Indianapolis: Sigma Theta Tau International, 2018

Medicare Benefit Policy Manual, Chapter 7, Home Health Services at: https://www.cms.gov/files/docum ent/se19027.pdf

MLN Matters Number: SE19027. (2019). *Overview of the Patient Driven Groupings Model.* Department of Health & Human Services.

PDGM Webpage at: https://www.cms.gov/Medicare/Medicare-Fee-for-Ser vice-Payment/HomeHealthPPS/HH-PDGM

Potter, James. Kavanagh, Mike. *The Successful Manager.* Potter Consulting LLC, 2020

The HRmeister. (2017, October 29). *Essential Elements of Employee Retention.* Retrieved from Lynch burg Regional SHRM: https://lrshrm.shrm.org/blog/2 017/10/essential-elements-employee-retention

ABOUT THE AUTHOR

As a nursing leader with over 35 years of total nursing experience, including nearly 30 years of progressive home care and hospice nursing management experience, 10 years in executive management and 14 years and counting in consulting, Julia H. Maroney RN MHSA realized there aren't a lot of resources for clinical managers to learn how to be successful in their careers. A registered nurse with a Masters in Health Services

Administration from St. Joseph's College in Maine, Julia hopes sharing her substantive experience in overall operations, including change leadership, quality improvement regulatory compliance and legislative advocacy influences the future leaders in home health and hospice agencies, guiding them to positive, successful careers. Besides writing, Julia founded a website that is a great resource for clinical managers featuring books, podcasts, newsletters, courses, colleague connection and career insight. She currently resides in Florida with her husband of 35 years and has a grown daughter and son-in-law.

Also By Julia H. Maroney

- The Successful Clinical Manager – Home Health

    - The Successful Clinical Manager – Home Health Workbook

- The Successful Clinical Manager – Hospice

    - The Successful Clinical Manager – Hospice Workbook

Made in the USA
Coppell, TX
15 June 2023

18094807R30144